THE PHYSICS OF TELEVISION

Born in Englewood, New Jersey, in 1911, DONALD G. FINK was educated at the Massachusetts Institute of Technology (B.Sc., 1933) and at Columbia University (M.Sc., 1942). He began building radio receivers as a boy and, at the age of sixteen, became a licensed radio amateur. Following graduation from M.I.T., Mr. Fink became an editor of *Electronics* magazine.

As Expert Consultant to the Office of the Secretary of War from 1943 to 1945, he arranged for the use of the Loran Navigation system by the United States and the Allied Forces. After the war he became editor in chief of *Electronics*.

Mr. Fink has represented the United States as technical advisor to the State Department Television Committee at international television conferences in Switzerland, France, Belgium, and England, and in 1958 was President of the Institute of Radio Engineers. Since 1959 he has been Director of Research of the Philco Corporation.

Mr. Fink has published articles in a number of technical journals, and he has prepared material for the television entries of the *Encyclopedia Britannica* and *Collier's Encyclopedia*. In addition, he is the author of many books, among which are *Radar Engineering* and *Television Engineering*.

DAVID M. LUTYENS, born in England in 1926, holds B.A. degrees in both science and history from Cambridge University. After serving as a major with the British Army in Germany, he was assistant master of physics at King Edward's College, Birmingham, and was the College Tutor, Winchester College. In 1957, Lutyens was awarded a Commonwealth Fund Fellowship to Harvard, in order to write a book and to study how science is taught in American universities and schools. While at Harvard he participated in the PSSC programs of classroom films and the Science Study Series. Lutyens returned to England in 1959 to become science editor of Penguin Books.

THE PHYSICS
OF TELEVISION

Donald G. Fink

and

David M. Lutyens

Published by
Anchor Books
Doubleday & Company, Inc.
Garden City, New York

Library of Congress Catalog Card Number 60–5925

THE SCIENCE STUDY SERIES

The Science Study Series offers to students and to the general public the writing of distinguished authors on the most stirring and fundamental topics of physics, from the smallest known particles to the whole universe. Some of the books tell of the role of physics in the world of man, his technology and civilization. Others are biographical in nature, telling the fascinating stories of the great discoverers and their discoveries. All the authors have been selected both for expertness in the fields they discuss and for ability to communicate their special knowledge and their own views in an interesting way. The primary purpose of these books is to provide a survey of physics within the grasp of the young student or the layman. Many of the books, it is hoped, will encourage the reader to make his own investigations of natural phenomena.

These books are published as part of a fresh approach to the teaching and study of physics. At the Massachusetts Institute of Technology during 1956 a group of physicists, high school teachers, journalists, apparatus designers, film producers, and other specialists organized the Physical Science Study Committee, now operating as a part of Educational Services Incorporated, Watertown, Massachusetts. They pooled their knowledge and experience toward the design and creation of aids to the learning of physics. Initially their effort was supported by the National Science Foundation, which has continued to aid the program. The Ford Foundation, the Fund for the Advancement of Education, and the Alfred P. Sloan Foundation have also given support. The Committee is creating a textbook, an extensive film series, a laboratory guide, especially designed apparatus, and a teacher's source book for a new integrated secondary school physics program which is undergoing continuous evaluation with secondary school teachers.

The Series is guided by a Board of Editors consisting of Paul F. Brandwein, the Conservation Foundation and Harcourt, Brace and Company; John H. Durston, Educational Services Incorporated; Francis L. Friedman, Massachusetts Institute of Technology; Samuel A. Goudsmit, Brookhaven National Laboratory; Bruce F. Kingsbury, Educational Services Incorporated; Philippe Le-Corbeiller, Harvard University; Gerard Piel, *Scientific American;* and Herbert S. Zim, Simon and Schuster, Inc.

CONTENTS

CHAPTER 1

Communication

Television is one of the major triumphs of applied science. Unfortunately, it is the fate of great inventions that as they become more and more an integral part of our daily life, they are taken increasingly for granted and cease to evoke the sense of wonder they really deserve. Electrical power, the airplane, man-made fibers, anti-biotics—all these have traveled the road to the mundane. Television has become, in fact, an accepted part of our existence more quickly than any other major scientific advance. Its growth has been nothing short of explosive. Social statisticians are fond of pointing out that there are now more television receivers than bathtubs in the United States. Television is affecting not only obvious things like entertainment customs and domestic routine, but educational techniques, scientific problems (such as how to get a picture of the far side of the moon)—and even our taste for beauty.

And the inevitable price has been paid. Such familiarity as this breeds, if not contempt, at least indifference. Yet the physics of television, which is the subject of this book, has fascinating interest. The story that lies behind the screen is a great deal more rewarding than many of those that appear on the screen. It has a plot more ingenious than most detective mysteries, more amazing than most science fiction, and more significant than many a political discussion.

To understand, in the first place, how that hypnotic picture appears in your living room we must face the enigma of wave motion. Light waves travel between the actor and the camera, and again between the receiver screen and your eye; radio waves travel through space between the transmitting tower and the antenna of your set; still other kinds of waves, called electrical signals, travel along hundreds of connecting wires and cables in the studio and network equipment.

Second, it is not possible to understand anything about electricity without delving into the structure of the atom and reading the biography of electrons. How to detach electrons from their parent atoms, and how subsequently to control their movement, are two of the central problems of all physics. Third, when we come in the last chapter to consider color TV, we shall find that there is a great deal more to seeing and analyzing colors than might at first be suspected. Nor must we neglect that miraculously ingenious human organ, the eye, to which the whole process is ultimately directed. The very possibility of television rests on such incidental peculiarities as the persistence of human vision. On the level of applied physics we shall need to become familiar with the vacuum tube, the number-one tool of modern electronics. We shall meet the photoelectric effect by which light is converted into electricity, and the mysterious property of fluorescence by which electricity may be converted back to light.

If these problems do not stir the curiosity and imagination of the reader, there is no point in his reading further. He would be better advised to tune to a local channel and accept, uncritically, the miracle of vision beyond the limits of sight. If the problems do interest the reader, then we shall start with him by considering the problem of communication in general and see where television fits into this larger setting.

Brain Waves

The aim of communication is to convey one person's thoughts and feelings to another. It is an everyday truism to say that one's thoughts and feelings are one's most private possessions; indeed, it is this very privacy which makes communication such a difficult and inaccurate business. A philosopher would rephrase this by saying that thoughts and feelings belong to a private world of individual consciousness. This internal world can be thought of as a complex bundle of data, primarily impressions from the senses, which we rapidly learn to organize into patterns. In so doing, we assign these impressions and patterns to the world external to ourselves, a world containing "things" like books, television sets, people, and so on. We think of each of these "things" as being the "cause" of certain sense impressions. This process rapidly becomes so instinctive that we soon attribute to the external physical world a reality as direct as that possessed by our private world of consciousness. The fact that babies, for instance, have to learn to correlate noises with particular visual objects shows that this process of identification is no mere fiction of the philosopher. An adult who receives his sight by surgery after being blind from birth also takes some time to sort out what seems to him at first to be merely a confusing jigsaw of vivid colored patches.

The physical events most closely related to one's conscious thoughts are certain electrochemical changes occurring in the cortex of the brain. We shall call these "brain waves" for short. It may be that brain waves cause conscious thoughts, as light waves falling on the eye undoubtedly cause electrical impulses to move along the optic nerve. On the other hand, it may be that the way a brain surgeon would describe your brain waves and the way you would describe your thoughts are merely two different ways of looking at the same events. Fortunately, we need not make a decision on this point, which has worried professional philosophers for more than two thousand years. For our purpose of understanding communication it matters only that brain waves are the nearest physical events to the thoughts we are trying to communicate.

Clearly, then, the ultimate in human communication would be for one person's brain waves somehow to be directly imprinted on the cerebral cortex of another. Then, provided the other person's brain was constructed to operate in the same way as that of the first, the act of communication would be as nearly perfect as we could ever expect it to be. As yet we cannot share each other's brain waves—perhaps fortunately—but progress in the study of the brain is very rapid, and it may happen someday that one person can make another "see" the starry heaven on a clear night by tickling the visual region of his cerebral cortex.

Flaws in Communication

In default of direct communication between brains, let us see how comparatively inefficient are man-made systems of communication. Let us start by supposing that you are trying to converse with your neighbor who lives in the house across the street. It is a cold day so that you both have your windows closed. You can see, but not hear. For your neighbor to convey his thoughts in these circumstances, he has to make some sort of visual "signal," which your eye will receive. Thus, two intermediaries are interposed between your brain and his. One of these (his hands, for example) we may call the transmitter; the other (your eyes) is the receiver. In these circumstances the amount of information which he can convey is strictly limited. By holding his head between his hands he may make you understand that he has a headache, but unless he is a skilled mimic you will not know whether this is as a result of an attack of the flu or of the previous night's revels.

The fact is that his hands are a very inefficient transmitter. Not only do they fail to convey his thoughts fast enough, but at every stage they coarsen them. His gestures are only very crude and inaccurate approximations to what he wishes to convey. Moreover, if the windows between you are covered with raindrops, this will interfere with your vision and will further coarsen, or distort, the visual information your eyes receive. Compared with the inefficiency of hands as transmitters, eyes are extremely efficient receivers. They can collect information with great rapidity, and preserve an amazing amount of its fine detail.

These criteria of *speed, accuracy,* and *distortion* can be applied generally to any system of communication. Let us now suppose that your neighbor is talking to you from the other side of a high garden wall. You can now hear but not see. Again we have two intermediaries, his voice as the transmitter and your ears as the receiver. Words are of course much more efficient transmitters than gestures, the most efficient as yet evolved by any animal species. Words are, in fact, the primary tool in man's domination of this planet.

Your neighbor can now satisfy your curiosity about the cause of his headache and tell you a great deal more besides. Yet we are well aware that even words are extremely inefficient as a means of communication when judged on a brain-to-brain standard. Whole books have been written on the debasement of thought by means of language. Poets and lovers know that many of man's noblest ideas border on the inexpressible. Words are also slow, at least relative to the speed at which information can be communicated by electronic machines. One only has to remember how little time there seems to be during a long-distance phone call!

When we move on to consider communication over longer distances, another criterion becomes important. This we call *power*. If your neighbor is on the other side of a lake, his voice probably will not be powerful enough to carry to you. If it is at night and he is signaling with a flashlight, the light may not be bright enough. We shall come to see that all forms of transmission, whether by sound, light, or any other form of radiation, involve the expenditure of energy. The faster the transmitter expends energy—that is, the more powerful it is—

the more readily it can span the distance to the receiver.

Besides these four criteria, there is one more concept fundamental to communication—indeed, to the acquirement of all information—that you will encounter in this book, especially in the later chapters. It is *modulation,* which you think of as "change" and take for granted in your daily life. If the palate, tongue, teeth, and lips could not modulate the air column from our lungs, there would be no speech, only a monotonous "whoooo" not even our mothers could interpret. Without modulation of the sound waves from the violin, piano, horn, or, again, the human voice, there would be no music. Without modulation—blinking—of the beam from our flashlight there would be no signal. And without modulation of radio waves, with which later on we shall deal at length, television would convey no information, only an exchange of meaningless energy. Modulation can be as simple a process as the switching on or off of an electric current, or, as we shall see, it can be an exceedingly complicated modification of wave movements. But, whatever its form, it is essential to communication.

If we are to choose among the many available means of communication, perhaps the first decision to be made is in what form the message shall cover the major portion of its journey. Sound travels slowly and only over relatively short distances, though it has the advantage of going around corners. Light travels at much higher speed (about a million times as fast). However, light is intercepted or scattered and absorbed by matter of all kinds, and it will go around corners only to a very limited extent. One of the questions we should be in a position to answer by the end of this book is *why* there should be these differences between sound and light. Radio waves (physically similar to light waves but of much longer wave length) can penetrate and pass around sizable solid objects. Again, why should this be?

Because of these contrasting properties long-distance communication takes place either by means of radio waves or by electric waves in wires. To use radio for communication we employ, of course, a transmitter and a receiver. These are really translating mechanisms. Just as the voice translates thoughts into a sound-wave code, so a microphone translates the sound-wave code into the code of electric current, and the transmitting aerial translates electrical current into radio waves. At the receiving end the receiving antenna decodes the radio waves into electrical impulses, the loud-speaker turns these back into sound waves, and the ear and brain decode sound waves into brain waves, or thoughts. With these additional links in the transmission chain it is more imperative than ever that coarsening, distortion, and loss of power at each stage should be minimized.

Pictures in Code

The secret of modern television was the invention and development of efficient encoders and decoders for the two unique stages that distinguish it from sound broadcasting. These stages are, of course, the encoding of light to electricity, and the decoding of electricity back to light.

Unfortunately, it is not sufficient merely to have ways of translating light to electricity and back again. We must also take account of the fact that in television we have only *one* channel to carry the picture. The optic nerve, which connects the eye to the brain, is marvelously more complex; it contains several hundred thousand separate fibers, or electric circuits, all which carry signals to the brain at the same time. Hence, in human vision each fiber of the optic nerve can take care of a small part of the picture, and we can take in the whole area of the picture at once. On a single television channel it is not feasible to carry hundreds of thousands of signals all at once, so we must fall back on the next best thing: we must carry the signals one after the other. We do this by dividing the picture up into tiny bits and transmitting information about each bit in turn.

We may borrow an analogy here from those enthusiasts who play chess at a distance. The board is divided up into numbered squares, and we can send messages such as, "Move Black Knight to Queen two," over the telephone. In this way one player can bring about a change in the visual appearance of his opponent's board, and the game can proceed as if both were playing on the same board.

In this way we begin to see how to transmit a still picture. We need not even mention which bit of the picture we are describing, provided that we always describe them in a systematic order. This could be any order. We might start at the bottom right-hand corner, proceed along the bottom and around the outside edge in a clockwise direction, thereafter moving gradually in toward the center in spiral fashion. In television we start at the top left-hand corner and cover the picture much as the eye scans the page of a book when reading. This similarity with reading has given this systematic way of traversing a picture the technical name *scanning*.

The next decision to be made is how many sub-divisions of the picture we must have. This will depend on how much fine detail we are prepared to sacrifice. Here is a very real example of the inevitable coarsening of a message by the act of communication.

If we wish to preserve all the fine details of the picture, we must break it up into a great many very tiny bits, one bit for each of the smallest details. But if we are content with a reasonably detailed reproduction, we may use a smaller number of larger subdivisions, and we will save ourselves a lot of expense and trouble in so doing. We may decide, in other words, that a somewhat coarse, but still generally satisfactory, communication of the picture best serves the economy of the television service. Such compromises between the quality of a service and the costs of providing it are at the core of all engineering.

Printed pictures are also reproduced by bits; that is, they are a collection of tiny black dots (Plate I). A high-quality picture, such as you see in the "slick paper" magazines, may contain millions of individual dots. This fine detail is appropriate for viewing at reading distance. Actually, at such close inspection, the eye does not view the picture all at once. It roves over the picture, taking in the printed dots in groups of several hundred thousand at a time. It can do no better, because the optic nerve has no more than several hundred thousand separate circuits to the brain.

Such a finely divided picture would be a costly waste in television because we do not view the television screen so closely. The compromise adopted by the engineers who designed our television system is a picture divided into about 200,000 bits.

Such a picture may appear rather coarse when we are tuning the receiver and are watching from a distance of only a foot or two. But it serves very well when we sit back in our chair, ten feet or so from the set.

Pictures in Motion

So much for the quality of our still picture. But we are not interested merely in still pictures. What happens if the details of the picture are constantly altering? The answer is that our scanning process must be very rapid in order to keep up. Imagine trying to describe verbally to a blind friend just how the advertisement signs in Times Square are changing. Words obviously are hopelessly slow in this context. Just *how* quickly do we need to scan our picture? This question ties up with the persistence of human vision.

We now understand that the television picture is assembled before our eyes, one picture bit at a time, arranged one after the other like the letters on this page. Only one picture bit is present at any instant of time. How, then, does the whole area of the screen appear as if it were lighted up continuously? The answer is that the brain retains the impression of the light entering the eye for about a tenth of a second after the light is shut off. Thus, if we assemble all the picture bits, one after the other, and complete the process in a tenth of a second or less, the perception of each bit persists while all the others are presented to the eye, and, presto, the piecemeal picture appears whole. If we take a much longer time to cover the screen, the picture falls apart into smaller portions.

Since we must reproduce each picture, then, in

less than a tenth of a second, we are, happily, able to transmit more than ten pictures per second. This provides the means for communicating a picture in motion, by presenting to the eye a rapid succession of many still pictures, as in the movies. Our mind holds on to each picture in the sequence, by persistence of vision, and we are unaware that a great many separate and slightly different still pictures are being offered to us during each second.

Actually, as we shall see later, television pictures are presented thirty times a second, and we recall that each one of them consists of 200,000 picture bits laid down on the screen one after the other. Simple multiplication reveals that the picture bits are communicated over the television system at the alarming rate of $30 \times 200,000$ or 6,000,000 per second. Every piece of television equipment, from studio to living room, must be capable of handling information at this fantastically fast pace. The translating from light to electricity, the electrical signals in wires and cables, the radio waves in space, and the retranslating from electricity to light —all must proceed as though pursued by ten thousand devils. No wonder the engineers have settled for 200,000 picture bits; any greater number would raise the transmission rate in proportion, and make every item of equipment that much more expensive to buy and more critical to operate.

In the early days of television much coarser pictures were tried, having only about 4000 picture bits. This was necessary because only mechanical methods of scanning were available, such as whirling discs with holes pierced in them (Figure 1), and these could not be made to move fast enough, or accurately enough, to produce a more detailed picture. Such coarse pictures were not sufficient to

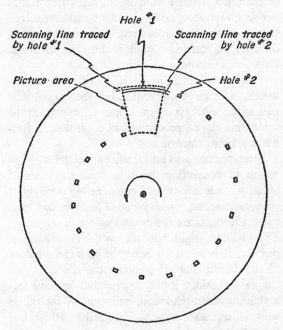

Fig. 1. Early television experiments used a rotating disc to scan the picture. The picture was focused on the disc in the area shown. Small holes, arranged in a spiral around the disc's edge, traced lines across the image, one line after another, and the light passing through each hole represented in succession the lights and shadows along each line. Such mechanical scanners could not televise a finely detailed image. Electronic scanners, which can cover millions of picture dots in a single second, have supplanted them.

satisfy the eye, after the initial wonder of seeing pictures at a distance wore off. To meet the million-per-second transmission speed of modern television, mechanical devices were, if not entirely out of the question, far too complicated and expensive to serve in the home.

The answer came, as we all know, with the advancing science of electronics. For the only objects that have the necessary speed and agility, and at the same time can be produced and controlled in simple ways, are *electrons.*

Electrons are also intimately connected with the means of converting the light from the scanned image into electricity, and regenerating the light at the receiving end, which we shall describe in Chapter 4. Electrons are the central actors in our story. They take us right into the world of subatomic physics. It is toward a better basic understanding of this world that we shall devote the next two chapters. At times it may appear that we have forgotten all about television, and some of the things we shall discuss may seem rather theoretical. But these chapters contain the essential groundwork to a proper understanding of the physics of television.

CHAPTER 2

Light

Television begins and ends with light. Light from a bank of lamps shines on the actors in the studio and is reflected from them. Entering the camera, it is focused and forms an image on the light-sensitive surface of the camera tube. At the receiving end light is transmitted from the viewing screen to your eye. Although this last stage may seem almost too obvious to mention, it is in fact extremely important, for we shall find that the physiological limitations of the human eye have a profound influence on the whole transmission process. Without them, television would hardly be possible. In this chapter, therefore, we shall examine the physics of light and human vision.

Let us start by asking the question, "What is light?" Light can be thought of primarily as a form of energy—so-called *radiant energy*. Most people think that they have a fairly satisfactory idea of what energy is. But the question, "What is energy?" is in fact so difficult to answer rigorously that it took scientists more than 150 years even to get their basic terms straight. It occupies a large part of any conventional physics course, and we cannot hope to give it full treatment here. Yet some digression is necessary to summarize those ideas which are presumed to be reasonably familiar to the reader. First, *work* is done whenever force is applied to a body to move it, the work being equal in amount to the product of the force and the distance moved. As a result of the work done on it, the body gains a corresponding amount of *energy*. Conversely, the agent that does the work loses an equal amount. Second, energy, like an accomplished actor, may appear in several different disguises. The two most familiar are *kinetic* energy, which is a property of any moving object by virtue of its *motion,* and *potential* energy, which belongs to an object by virtue of its *position.* Thus a television set in a second-floor bedroom is said to have more potential energy than one in a ground-floor living room because work had to be done against the force of gravity in carrying it upstairs. We shall find, however, that it is better to regard potential energy as the property of a *system.* By this term, scientists mean any arbitrary region of the universe that they find convenient to study in isolation. In our example it is really not the television set which has gained potential energy but the system containing the set *and* the earth. Similarly, when an electron in an atom is moved away from the nucleus, against the force of electrical attraction, the potential energy of the atom as a whole increases.

Other forms of energy—thermal, electrical, chemical, and so on—appear at first to be more mysterious. However, they can in fact all be expressed in terms of the movements and positions of atomic or subatomic particles and therefore reduced to a summation of the kinetic and potential energy of these tiny objects. The energy of wave motion is another matter. For a wave need not involve the movement of particles at all; light travels satisfactorily through interstellar space. In all previous examples energy was carried from place to place in the transfer of matter, as when the hero in a television play hurls a china vase at his approaching adversary, or when air moves from the blades of a studio fan off screen to rustle the hair of some languorous heroine. With wave motion energy is transferred without the passage of matter. When we say that light is a form of energy, part of what we mean is that when it passes from one place to another it involves the transfer of energy.

Waves and/or Particles

Is it best to think of light as a wave motion or as a stream of particles? Though most people would vote strongly for wave motion, the evidence suggests that the answer is much less simple. Indeed, the conflict of descriptions is as old as the days of Isaac Newton, who, incidentally, favored particles. Although Thomas Young, Augustin Fresnel, and others seemed for a time to have proved that light was really a wave motion, about the beginning of this century increasing evidence began to be unearthed which could only be explained in terms of non-material particles.

What exactly does this mean? Are both theories right, wrong, or merely incomplete? Can we use either indiscriminately? The great English physicist Sir Lawrence Bragg used to tell his undergraduates that he preferred the wave theory on Mondays, Wednesdays, and Fridays, and the particle theory on Tuesdays, Thursdays, and Saturdays! Yet the situation is not quite so arbitrary. To describe radiant energy as wave or particle is rather like conveying information about a person either by means of a photograph or a verbal character sketch. Each is better than the other for different purposes. A photograph is more informative than any written description if we are concerned with the person's physical features. On the other hand, words can tell us more about his character and past history, even though the presence, say, of a gold watch chain stretched across an ample stomach may suggest something. The first point to note is that both descriptions, pictorial and verbal, are by themselves inadequate. The actual individual is more complex than either, more different from our preconceived notions than perhaps we realize. Second, both descriptions, though incomplete, must be consistent with each other. We should know something was wrong if we read that our individual was seventy-five years old, and then received a picture of a young man in the prime of life.

So it is with the wave and particle models. Both tell us partial truths about light. Both are consistent with each other. Thus there is a strict measurable relationship between the frequency of the wave and the energy of the particle, or *photon,* as it is called. This relation is expressed by Albert Einstein's famous relation $E = hf$, where h is a basic numerical constant of the universe, known as Planck's constant after its discoverer, Max Planck. The number of wave crests passing a given point each second, f, is the frequency of light (considered as a wave), and E is the energy of the photon (considered as a particle). In this and other senses the two theories have been integrated into one. Yet light is neither one thing nor the other. It is more unimaginable still, and as yet the only words we have to describe it at all accurately are mathematical symbols. We shall find the need to speak of light in both disguises during the coming chapters.

It is well known that white light is a mixture of colored constituents into which it can be separated by passage through a prism. How do these colored lights differ from each other? Let us use the wave model first. Normally it is said that red light differs from blue in that they have different wave lengths, but a more satisfactory distinction is that of frequency. (See Plate II and Figure 1a for explanation of these terms.) This is because the wave length (the distance from crest to crest or trough to trough) of any given colored light is not always the same. Should the velocity of light (c) alter, as it does, for instance, when light passes from one transparent medium to another, it will be seen from the relation of wave length (λ) and frequency that the product ($c = \lambda f$) must alter. When this happens, the frequency does not change; the wave length does. Light waves have frequencies of about 10^{14} cycles per second. This is an almost inconceivably large number; 10^{14} is a hundred millions of millions. The corresponding wave lengths are almost inconceivably small, about half of a millionth of a meter.

The energy of a photon can be expressed in any unit from calories to kilowatt hours, but for reasons that will soon become apparent it will be much the most convenient for us in this book to use the unit *electron volt,* abbreviated "ev." We shall define this when we have become better acquainted with both electrons and volts; at this stage we simply state that the energy of visible light photons varies from 2 to 4 ev.

We must note that the variation in wave frequency and photon energy does not stop at the

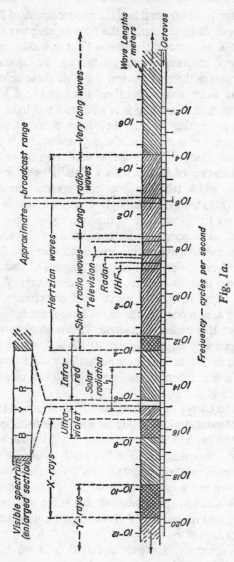

Fig. 1a.

limits of visible light. Beyond the blue end of the spectrum (Figure 1a) are forms of radiation with still higher energies, ultraviolet (up to 150 ev), X-rays (up to 40,000 ev), and gamma rays (beyond 40,000 ev). Beyond the red are forms with lower frequencies, infrared (down to 10^{12} cycles per second), and radio waves (less than 10^{12} cycles per second).

Atoms as a Source of Light

Getting back to light, we must now investigate a second question. What produces it? This involves the very basic problem of how light and matter interact. Essentially, the question is, "How can an atom produce a photon?" Once more we are forced to go off on a major digression, this time to equip ourselves with a working knowledge of the atom.

In this nuclear age, there can be few readers who are not aware that each atom has a nucleus. Around this central core, which is heavy and compact and carries a positive electric charge, there move electrons of negative charge and comparatively negligible mass. The atoms of all elements are built on this same general pattern; the different kinds of atoms differ in the number and arrangement of the planetary electrons. The number of electrons is determined by the size of the positive charge on the nucleus, since the atom as a whole is electrically neutral.

If this were a book on the atom bomb, we should now forget about the planetary electrons and concentrate exclusively on the nucleus. As it is for the purpose of understanding the physics of television, we shall do exactly the reverse. We shall ignore the

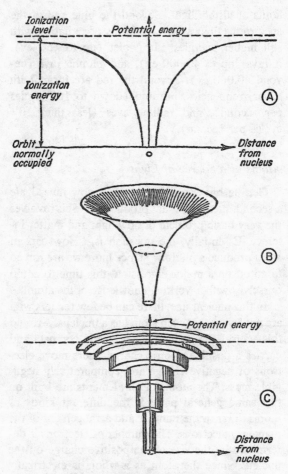

*Fig. 2. The "potential well" inhabited by orbit-
ing electrons is schematically pictured in these
three diagrams. The curve in A shows that the
farther the electron orbit is from the nucleus, the
greater must be the potential energy. B shows
how the curve, extending in all directions about
the nucleus of the atom, forms a "well" within*

nucleus and fix attention on the behavior of the electrons.

Now, just as there is a mysterious dualism in the nature of light, so there is in the behavior of electrons. Electrons usually, but not always, behave as though they were minute particles. Often they seem to have the properties of a wave motion. For the moment, however, we shall choose the particle model, in which electrons resemble nuclear sputniks. The force of electrical attraction, which is always present between opposite electric charges, holds them in their orbits. This is, of course, the analogue of gravitational attraction in the case of earth satellites. A useful way of describing the operation of this force is to say that there exists around the nucleus an electric *field,* the intensity of the field at any given point being a measure of the force acting on the electron. Around the earth is a similar gravitational field.

Just as it requires work to lift a satellite to a greater distance from the earth, so it does to lift an electron farther away from the nucleus. This work is stored as increased potential energy of the whole atom. If we draw a graph of this potential energy against distance from the nucleus, we get a curve of the shape of Figure 2, and since this curve applies symmetrically in all directions around the nucleus, the over-all surface is that of a trumpet

which the electron is trapped until energy, transferred from an external source, pushes the electron over the edge, and it escapes from its parent atom. C shows that the electron can, in fact, occupy only certain energy levels. These quantized steps represent the allowed orbits, between which the electron jumps as it absorbs or gives off energy.

with its bell end up. We shall refer to this as a potential *energy well*. Any electron moving within the
confines of the well is called a "bound" electron
because, unless energy is given to the system from
some outside source, the electron cannot climb up
the wall of the well and escape from the field of its
parent atom. However, if given a sufficient amount
of energy, it can leave the field permanently and so
become a *free* electron. The rest of the atom then is
left with a positive charge equal to that on the electron, and is called an *ion*. The process of electron
escape is called *ionization*.

While still bound to the atom, the electrons cannot circulate in just any old orbit. One of the most
seminal discoveries of twentieth-century physics
was that there are definite restrictions on the *energy
levels* of electrons in atomic orbits. It appears that
they can only differ by discrete amounts of energy.
It is not possible for an electron in one orbit to
increase its distance from the nucleus by an infini-
tesimal amount. It must "jump" to a new orbit.
The orbits of bound electrons are thus said to be
quantized, and when an electron receives enough
energy to jump into a higher quantized orbit the
atom is said to be *excited*. Quantization is a phenomenon rarely met with outside the subatomic
world. It has no analogy in large-scale macroscopic
physics, or in our workaday world.

The various quantized orbits around a nucleus
can accommodate differing numbers of electrons.
As a general rule, the orbits of lowest energy are
preferentially occupied. As we consider atoms in
order of increasing mass, that is, as we proceed
from element to element in the table of the chemical elements, the lower levels in the potential well
become progressively filled up. As it were, the ring-

side seats around the nucleus are occupied first. However, there are always upper levels which are vacant, and into which an electron may be made to jump by exciting the atom with an external source of energy. An atom will remain in this excited state only for a very short time, about 10^{-8} second, and then the electron normally will lose energy by radiation and revert to the atom's lowest empty orbit. When we energize matter in ways to be described shortly, we are in fact producing (among other effects) a hectic dance of electrons jumping orbits in trillions of atoms simultaneously.

How does an atom gain the energy necessary for its excitation or ionization? And in what disguise does it liberate the surplus energy when it reverts to its normal unexcited state? To begin an answer to the latter question first, one of the commonest ways in which an atom may unburden itself of unwanted energy is by emitting a photon. The energy of the photon will, of course, depend on which particular electron jump is involved.

The shape of the energy well shows that orbits near the nucleus are separated by energies of many ev, whereas those nearer the outside of the atom are, energetically, much closer together. Jumps between these latter orbits will, in fact, produce photons with energies of 2 to 4 ev, or visible light.

Energy and Light

Here, then, is a first answer to the question, "What produces light?" We can observe such a process in a neon advertising sign or a mercury vapor lamp. Both consist essentially of a glass tube filled with the appropriate gas or vapor at very low pressure. When an electrical voltage is applied to the tube, some of the atoms are ionized. The resulting free electrons and positive ions are accelerated by the force of the voltage and, because of their opposite charges, move in opposite directions. They collide with un-ionized atoms, transferring some of their energy to them in the process.

Two kinds of collision can occur. Sometimes there is an elastic collision, such as would occur between two perfectly elastic rubber balls. In these the target atom takes up the extra energy in kinetic form; that is, its velocity increases, but its internal arrangement is unchanged. The chaotic random motion of the gas atoms thus becomes more violent; the gas is heated up. In other cases, however, the energy is transferred by an inelastic process. The target atom then stores the extra energy in potential form; that is, one of its electrons jumps to a higher level and the atom becomes excited.

Now let us consider the photon energy release that very quickly follows as the electron falls back into a lower-energy orbit. Since the electron jump is quantized, only photons of a particular energy will be radiated. And since of all the possible orbit jumps there are always a few that occur much more easily than the rest, all the excited gas atoms emit photons of these few preferred energies.

Switching to the wave model, we see that the light emitted is therefore restricted to a few selected frequencies characteristic of the particular element concerned. This explains why neon glows orange-red, while mercury vapor glows blue-green. Any such group of frequencies is called a *spectrum,* and one with specially preferred frequencies such as we have been discussing is called a *line spectrum.*

Sunlight is very different. Apart from the presence of certain dark lines in the sun's spectrum, which we may in this context ignore, sunlight is composed of a continuous range of colors, not merely a few selected ones. It contains light of every frequency within the visible limits, and its spectrum is therefore referred to as *continuous*. This appears to violate the ideas of quantization which so successfully explain the emission of light from a glowing mercury source. The explanation is that in the case of the sun we are dealing with very much higher temperatures. Temperature is simply a measure of the average kinetic energy of the gas particles in their chaotic random motion. Thus the hotter the gas, the more energetic the collisions between its particles.

One process involved here is important in television. In some of the inelastic collisions enough energy is absorbed by one of the participants not merely to excite it but to raise an electron completely out of the energy well—in other words, to cause ionization. Moreover, since there is now no externally applied voltage to sweep the electron and ion in opposite directions, the electron is free to fall back into the field of its parent ion or of an adjacent one. Now for the crucial point: *when an electron is free, it is no longer quantized*. It can pick up or lose by elastic collision *any* amount of kinetic energy. Therefore, when it drops back into the energy well, it can do so from *any* energy level even though its final resting orbit is quantized. Consequently it is possible for photons of any intermediate energy—light waves of any frequency—to be emitted.

Much the same considerations apply to a glowing solid, such as the hot metal wire that forms the filament of the ordinary light bulb. As we shall see in more detail in the next chapter, the atoms in a metal are permanently ionized, and all contribute to a pool of so-called conduction electrons not specifically bound to any one parent atom, and their energy changes are not quantized. Again, therefore, the emission spectrum is continuous. Yet it is well known that the color of a metal changes as its temperature is raised, whether we heat it in a flame or by passing an increasingly large electric current through it. The metal (which first radiates heat only in the infrared) gradually glows red, orange, yellow, and finally white-hot. Although the eye cannot distinguish the components of the white-hot radiation, it is a continuous spectrum with the frequency of the most intense radiation progressively increasing. As the temperature rises, the average energy of the particles, whether electrons or ions, increases correspondingly. Collisions become more violent, and so do the energy changes which produce the photons.

This example leads us to a general principle of great importance. We have seen that photons may be emitted whenever electrons change their energy. Sometimes, as in the quantized jumps within an atom, it is primarily a change of potential energy. But at others, as with the conduction electrons of a metal, it is primarily a change of kinetic energy. Now to change its kinetic energy a body must change its velocity or, in other words, accelerate. It is a basic generalization of classical physics that *whenever a free electron accelerates, radiation is emitted.*

How Atoms Reflect Light

We have now given some answers to the question, "What produces light?" They all appear to be variations on a central theme, that of electron-photon interaction. A further variant of this theme provides the explanations of light's behavior when it is reflected from a surface. Here a major difference is that the cause of the atomic excitation is not an electron or ion, but a photon. Reflection is relevant to television in that it is light, reflected from the clothes and features of the actors and from the materials of the set, which enters the camera lens.

Reflection is an extremely complex phenomenon, so we will begin with the simplest possible case, that of light falling on a metallic mirror. Here the vast majority of the incident light is reflected, and furthermore without any loss of the detailed image. Points on the metal surface receiving light of low intensity also reflect light of low intensity —in other words, "appear" dark.

A sheet of white paper behaves differently. To begin with, the surface is much rougher and less homogeneous. One can see the tangled mass of fibers even under an optical microscope. The result is that the photons penetrate below the surface, do not emerge in the same regular fashion, but instead become scattered in many directions. The detailed image is thus lost. Yet the *color* of this diffusely reflected light is always the same as that of the incident light. ("Re-emission" might more precisely describe this process than reflection, but, having made the point, in this book we shall stick to the common word.) During reflection from a white substance the relative number of photons of different energies is not altered. In wave language, the intensity distribution of frequencies is unchanged.

A neutral gray surface is one that reflects only a fraction of the photons of any given frequency.

This fraction is, however, the same for all frequencies; so again the intensity *distribution* does not alter. A black surface is one that does not reflect any photons at all within the visible frequency range. What happens to the photons which are not reflected? They are absorbed. So we must next try to picture how absorption works.

Suppose that the incident photon has exactly the energy of a preferred electron jump in one of the surface atoms. It will be absorbed by means of an inelastic collision, the atom accepting the energy by becoming excited. This is the reverse of the emission process in the case of a line spectrum. Why, then, should not the excited atom immediately reradiate a photon identical to the incident one? The answer is that although from our previous point of view the lifetime of an excited atom, 10^{-8} second, was exceedingly short, from the point of view of atomic processes it is exceedingly long. There is plenty of time for lots of other things to happen before the excited atom decides that it must radiate. For example, the period of vibration of atoms within the framework of a molecule is often of the order of 10^{-15} second, which means that they will vibrate back and forth about ten million times during the life of the excited atom. Now an excited atom has an electron displaced from its normal position, and this will automatically alter the electric field in the neighborhood. This may attract or repel a neighboring atom as the case may be, but at any rate will alter the amplitude of its vibration. Just as you have to do work—give it a push—to set a pendulum swinging more violently, so the excited atom does work when it modifies the vibration of its neighbors. This involves it in a loss of energy, and this energy is progressively passed on to other atoms—in other words, dissipated or "bled" throughout the array of atoms. By the time it comes to radiate, the remaining energy available is equivalent to a photon of much lower frequency, if, indeed, a photon is emitted at all. Thus a black substance is such an efficient absorber that it rapidly gets hot, one symptom of which is that it reradiates photons in the infrared region.

How about colored substances? These selectively absorb photons of preferred energies. Sometimes it is the basic material itself which does this; for instance, solid gold absorbs primarily in the higher energy regions, thus reflecting the photons of lower energies and appearing yellow. More usually, substances are colored because of the presence of small numbers of pigment molecules, and it is these which do the absorbing. Depending on the detailed construction of the pigment molecule, the permitted electron jumps will differ in energy, and photons of different energies will be absorbed. In this way one actress may choose to wear a dress of delicate blue, in which the pigments absorb preferentially in the lower frequencies, while a second may prefer a ravishing red dress, which absorbs primarily in the higher frequency range.

Unfortunately these carefully premeditated effects will be largely lost on viewers of black-and-white television, and we are now in a position to see why. The black-and-white camera merely records the over-all *intensity* of the light. If in addition we make the fair approximation that it is equally sensitive to the entire visible frequency range, it will not matter whereabouts in the spectrum absorption is occurring but merely how much. To viewers and critics, both dresses may well appear an indistinguishable shade of gray.

Fluorescence: Invisible to Visible

It will probably seem that even for a chapter concerned primarily with theoretical groundwork we have strayed unduly far from the straight and narrow path. But we are now in a position to conclude with three further variants of photon-electron interaction which are of direct relevance to the television process.

The first of these is fluorescence, the process by which light is produced on your television screen. This may be regarded as a rather special case of reflection in which the incoming energy is not visible. If there is some factor that makes the elastic bleeding of energy from an excited atom more difficult, then the chances of its reradiating a photon will be increased. If some energy loss still occurs, the frequency of the radiated photon will be lower than that of the incident photon. Certainly it can never be higher; and in all cases it will be quantized. We should also expect the process to be "slow," that is to say, requiring of the order of 10^{-8} second.

All these conditions are fulfilled by fluorescence, which is defined as the production of visible light as a result of exposure to some invisible agency. Such agencies may be photons of higher than visible energies, such as ultraviolet rays or X-rays, or alternatively they may be particles of sufficiently high energy. Thus, when a beam of free electrons impinges on coated glass it causes it to fluoresce.

From the point of view of practical television this process is of central importance, for it provides the crossover link back from the world of electric current to the world of light. In the picture tube of the receiver the screen is covered with a fluorescent material, and by spraying this with a jet of electrons we can make it glow. Whenever the jet is more intense, the material glows more brightly. In this way it is possible to see how a detailed image might be created. In black-and-white receivers the particular fluorescent material chosen glows with a slightly bluish light. However, different materials fluoresce with different colors, and this, of course, has important implications for color television.

The Photoelectric Effect: Light into Electricity

Fluorescence is the process by which free electrons generate light photons. If there happened to be a reverse effect whereby light photons could liberate free electrons, not only would this round off our picture of photon-electron interaction in a most satisfactory manner, but it would also provide the means of converting the visual image into an electric current in the television camera. Such a mechanism does in fact exist; it is the famous "photoelectric effect" (which incidentally was the subject of Einstein's first major scientific publication).

The photoelectric effect is the emission of free electrons, called photoelectrons, from the surface of a metal when this is irradiated by light. It occurs in all metals, though with varying ease. Clearly, to liberate an electron a certain minimum of energy will be required to do work against the forces binding it to the surrounding positive ions in the metal. We may call this the *escape energy,* and this is what varies from metal to metal. Any excess energy that the electron may have received, it will retain as kinetic energy. In the photoelectric effect the source of energy is a photon.

If we are armed with the concept of a photon, the experimental facts of photoelectricity are not difficult to interpret. Indeed, historically they were so difficult to explain by the wave theory of light that it was the photoelectric effect which caused Einstein to postulate the photon's existence.

First, it was found that only light above a certain critical frequency caused *any* electrons to be emitted. We can now see that this is because at lower frequencies the incident photons cannot impart the minimum escape energy. Second, above this lower limit the kinetic energy of the photoelectrons varied not with the intensity of the light but with its frequency. No matter how intense the beam of light which shone on the metal, the kinetic energy of the electrons did not alter. Again this is explicable if light is regarded as a stream of photons, for the higher their energy (frequency) the more they will give to the electron, since quantization makes the energy exchange an all-or-nothing process. But merely increasing its intensity does not give each individual photon more energy, and this cannot therefore affect the kinetic energy of the photoelectron. What such an increase in intensity can do, and this was the third experimental finding, is to increase the number of incident photons and therefore of photoelectrons. Since free electrons in motion constitute an electric current, we can restate the last point as follows: The magnitude of the electric current produced is proportional to the intensity of the incident light.

Practical use is made of this fact in the photoelectric cell, but it is also even more subtly employed in the television camera. We shall see how this works in detail in Chapter 4, but at this stage at least the principle is clear. By focusing the visual image on a photoelectric surface, we shall cause electrons to be liberated in numbers directly proportional to the brightness of each particular point of the image. This will record in electronic terms the light and shade of the visual picture we wish to televise.

Light Waves into Brain Waves

The third and last variant of the photon-electron interaction theme is really a special case of the photoelectric effect. This is the transformation of light into nerve impulses within the eye. Here we find a more complicated electron-photon interaction in which chemistry plays a part, akin to the chemistry of photography.

The retina of the eye is made up of over a hundred million tiny photoreceptors, the rods and cones. These are connected to the fibers of the optic nerve. In the center of the eye's field of view each cone is connected to an individual fiber; in the outer regions of the field the rods and cones are connected to each fiber in groups of a hundred or more. The light-sensitive material of the rods which detect very weak light has been isolated. It is called visual purple, and it resembles the photosensitive dyestuffs used in photographic films. Unlike the emulsion dyes used in photography, however, visual purple possesses a reversible chemical reaction and hence is capable of continually renewing its sensitivity to light.

When light falls on visual purple, it causes chemical changes by transferring the outer electrons from one type of atom to another, among the chemical compounds of the pigment. These changes leave some of the atoms ionized, and these are capable of generating and carrying electric currents, much like the ions in the electrolyte of a storage battery. Thus, as the retina is stimulated by light, its photoreceptors generate electric impulses which affect the optic nerve fibers to which they are connected. The time scale of such electrochemical reactions is very much greater than the electron-orbit jump previously mentioned in this chapter. Consequently, the speed of the electric impulses as they travel along the nerve to the brain is incomparably slow—only 100 meters per second—compared with the speed of light (300 million meters per second). This comparative sluggishness explains the marked tendency of the photoreceptors and nerves to continue to transmit impulses after the light stimulus is removed. This effect (visual persistence) is one we could not possibly do without in television.

Let us now quickly look back over the considerable journey we have traveled in this chapter. We have made a number of digressions, but our primary concern throughout has been with light, since this plays such a central role in the television process. We began by asking what light is. We found that, along with other comparable radiations, it can be described in terms of two different vocabularies, wave language and particle language. Both give incomplete but mutually consistent and complementary pictures. We next introduced the main theme of the chapter, the interaction between radiation and matter, essentially the duel between photons and electrons. Variations on this theme account not only for the emission of light (by the studio lamps), but its reflection (from the surfaces of the objects to be televised); its conversion into an electric current (at the light-sensitive surface of the camera tube); its regeneration from free electrons (in the fluorescent material of the picture tube of the receiver); and finally its absorption on the retinal surface of the viewer's eye.

As yet the electronic middle stages of the process still remain dark and mysterious. There are a number of "black boxes" waiting to be examined both in the impressive banks of equipment around the studio and transmitting station, and in the cabinet which graces the corner of the living room. But first we must read the biography of the electron with as much care as we have read that of the photon. It is to this task that we now turn.

CHAPTER 3

Electricity

Most electrons spend the vast majority of their existence as nuclear satellites. As gravity ties the earth to the solar system, so electrical attraction ties the electron to the atom. However, we have seen that it is possible for an electron to be detached from its parent atom and for it to retain its independent status for a significant period of time. For such we have coined the description "free" electron. Whenever free electrons move in ordered fashion, there results a wholesale transfer of negative electric charge, and this is a flow of electric current.

In this chapter we are essentially concerned with how free electrons can conveniently be made to move in an orderly way; in other words, how electric currents may be generated and manipulated. We shall begin by explaining a few essential terms, and then make a general distinction among three different kinds of current flow—those arising in a solid, gas, and vacuum. These three types of electron flow are as vital to the television set as blood circulation is to the body.

Electrons, Current and Voltage

First, then, how shall we express current flow quantitatively? Current strength is a measure of the rate at which electric charge flows past a certain point. Mathematically, $I = Q/t$, where I is the symbol for current, and Q is the charge passing a given point in time t. The normal unit is the ampere, and when a steady current of 1 ampere flows along a wire, approximately 6×10^{18} electrons pass through a cross section of the wire each second. Even with the minute current of a millionth of an ampere, there are still more than a million million electrons passing each second. Clearly, we must get used to thinking in terms of very large numbers of electrons.

Second, we need some measure of what is forcing the electrons to migrate. This influence is the *potential difference*, or *voltage*, which is often described as "electrical pressure." It will pay us to try to get a precise grasp of this all-important concept. Electrons move only when they are subjected to an unbalanced electric force. We have already adopted the term "field" to describe how this force varies from point to point in any given situation, say, near the surface of a metal. Figure 3 is a pictorial representation of one such electrostatic field. It helps us to predict how an electron will behave. If left to itself, the electron will roll down the energy slope toward the metal surface. In doing so, the potential energy of the system will decrease, say, by E_1. Conversely, if the electron is to be "lifted" back out again, this will require some other energy source to increase the potential energy of the system by the same amount, E_1. (Compare

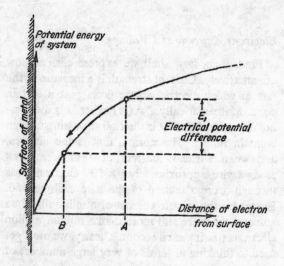

Fig. 3. The potential energy curve of an electron outside its parent atom. At the left is a positively charged metal surface which attracts the free electron. To move the electron away from the surface, from B to A, we must increase its potential energy by the amount E_1. The work done in moving the electron is the electrical potential difference, or "voltage difference," as we commonly call it.

the energy well of Figure 2, page 32.) *Work* will have to be done *on* the system. The electrical potential difference between A and B (a phrase which now speaks for itself) is simply defined as the work that has to be done to move a unit charge from one point to the other.

When one of the two points, say, B, has zero potential energy, the word "difference" is tacitly dropped, and instead we refer simply to the potential of A. For the point B actually to have zero potential, it would have to be at an infinite distance from all electric charges. For most practical purposes the earth ("electrical ground") is used as a reference body, and we shall even find it convenient on occasion to refer all potentials in a circuit to some quite arbitrarily chosen zero point, even if this is itself at a high potential to the earth. This potential difference, or voltage drop, is essential to a system in which electrons migrate. It implies work, and work implies a force.

In passing we may now define the unit *electron volt,* previously introduced on page 29. This is a unit of energy or work; it equals the amount required to move one electron through a potential difference of one volt. It is not the same as the volt itself, as might at first be thought, because (for historical reasons) the *unit of charge* used in defining a volt is different from and very much larger than one electron.

The third introductory concept is that of resistance (Figure 4). This is a measure of the opposition offered by the medium to the passage of electrons. It is quantitatively defined by the famous Ohm's Law: current I equals voltage V divided by resistance R, or $I = V/R$. From our point of view the importance of this is as follows. If we allow current to flow through a circuit that includes a poor conductor, which is called a resistor, we find that a voltage drop exists between the ends of the *resistor*. When the current varies, we find that this voltage drop changes proportionally. Its value v at any instant can be calculated from a rearrangement of Ohm's Law, $v = iR$, where i is the instantaneous value of the current. Since R is constant, it is seen that v exactly mirrors i, keeping in step with it instant by instant. This is an extremely useful rela-

tionship. One application of it is to convert the
"picture current" emerging from the camera into
the corresponding "picture voltage," which can be
conveniently amplified and transmitted over wires
and cables.

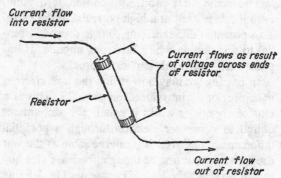

*Fig. 4. A resistor is a device that offers electrical
resistance, or friction, to the passage of current.
To make the current flow, voltage must be applied across the ends of the resistor. Conversely,
when a current is forced to go through a resistor,
a voltage appears across its ends.*

The mechanism of resistance varies from medium to medium, but in general it may be thought
of as a kind of electrical friction. Whenever an
electron with kinetic energy passes near another
charged body, such as an ion, it will interact with
it and lose energy in the process. In the many repe-
titions of this process work is done in forcing the
electrons through the medium. In other words,
there is a progressive drop in voltage along the path
of the electrons.

Beyond Ohm's Law

Armed with the sword of voltage and the shield of resistance, we may now venture forth into the realm of the solid and observe the restless fate of electrons therein! From an electrical point of view solids may be divided into two general categories—insulators, which do not permit a flow of electrons through them, and conductors, which do. This distinction is only one of degree. From the best insulators (such as porcelain and rubber) at one extreme, it passes through intermediate substances (like human tissue) to excellent conductors (such as metals) at the other extreme. What makes one solid a better conductor than another is, of course, its different electronic configuration, but this is now considerably more complicated than that of a single isolated atom such as we considered in the last chapter.

Perhaps it would be best to examine first what happens when two isolated atoms approach each other. At a certain separation, as measured between their nuclei, their two electric fields begin to interact. Figure 5 shows how, if a combination occurs with the formation of a molecule, the inward-facing walls of the individual energy wells have been broken down to some extent. Electrons with energy levels within the black shaded region can now move freely between both atoms, though they cannot escape from the system altogether. Such electrons are said to occupy *molecular* orbits rather than atomic ones.

In a piece of metal we have not merely two but an enormous number of atoms interacting with each other and bound together in what is called a

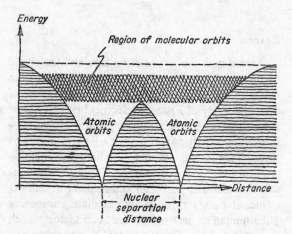

Fig. 5. When two isolated atoms come close together, their potential wells interact as shown at the center of the diagram. Electrons inhabiting orbits within the cross-hatched area are then free to move between the atoms, although they cannot escape from the system comprising the two atoms.

lattice. There are about 3×10^{23} atoms of copper in a piece of that metal the size of a penny (approximately ½ cubic centimeter). There are, therefore, this number of individual wells joined together. Some of the electrons are free to move anywhere within the limits of the solid and are no longer in any real sense bound to any individual atom. This is why we are justified in regarding the atoms in a metallic solid as permanently ionized, and contributing to a common "pool" of so-called *conduction electrons*. The word "pool" is quite appropriate since for most electrical purposes we can forget the existence of the individual energy wells with their still-bound electrons. The *energy* dia-

gram resembles a shallow pool in which the conduction electrons are free to move without restric-
tion. Of course, the electrons do not float on top of
the metal in any positional sense. They permeate
the whole solid and are constantly colliding with
the ions and among themselves.

When a voltage is applied at opposite ends of a
metal wire, the conduction electrons are accelerated toward the positively charged end. Repeated
elastic collisions occur with ions, slowing the electrons down. But between adjacent collisions they
are again accelerated. Thus occurs an over-all migration of electrons along the wire—that is, an electric current. But it is important to realize that the
current moves very much faster along the wire than
the electrons. The electrons' drift velocity, their
movement along the wire, is very slow indeed, even
compared with molasses on a cold day. To bring
this point home, we will make an approximate cal-
culation. In Figure 6 we consider a current of 1
ampere passing through a copper bar of cross section equal to that of a penny, about 3 sq. cm. We
have seen that any one penny contains nearly
3×10^{23} atoms. If each of these atoms is ionized,
there are the same number of conduction electrons
per penny. We also know that for a current of 1
ampere, 6×10^{18} electrons must cross any one
cross section of the wire each second. If we imagine all the electrons in the penny moving along as
a group, the distance they will have to move, in
proportion to the penny's thickness, to achieve the
necessary rate of flow is simply $\dfrac{6 \times 10^{18}}{3 \times 10^{23}}$ or two
one-hundred-thousandths of the thickness. In
other words, the net shift of the electrons in one

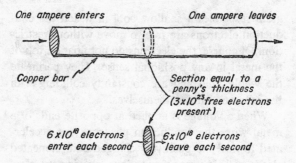

One ampere enters   *One ampere leaves*

Copper bar

Section equal to a penny's thickness (3×10^{23} free electrons present)

6×10^{18} electrons enter each second   *6×10^{18} electrons leave each second*

Net shift of electrons per second equals .00002 of penny's thickness

Fig. 6. *Passage of an electric current of one ampere through a copper bar having a cross section equal to that of a penny. Although an enormous number of electrons must pass through each cross section in a second, there are so many atoms in the bar that the electrons themselves move only a tiny fraction of an inch during each second. Nevertheless, all the free electrons in the bar move at once, and the current moves out of the bar at almost the same instant it enters the opposite end.*

second is less than the thickness of the thinnest paper!

Yet the signals may be propagated with speeds approaching that of light, or 3×10^8 meters in one second. How do we explain the discrepancy? The answer is that once more we are concerned with a form of wave motion. As in all wave motions the speed of the wave itself is quite different from the speed of the motion of the medium. Very crudely, we may think of an electron moving under the influence of voltage and nudging its neighbor, which then nudges *its* neighbor farther down the wire, and so on. As a rumor can travel faster than the individuals who spread it, so here the energy travels faster along the wire than the electrons which exchange it. What is propagated with the speed of light is the act of nudging, or, when millions of electrons are behaving similarly, a region where the electrons are more closely packed than normal.

Again it will help to be slightly more quantitative. Let us apply a voltage which varies as in Figure 7; that is, it is alternately on and off for a

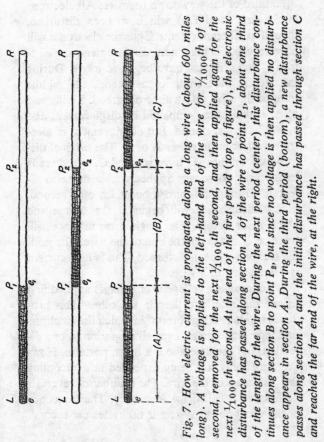

Fig. 7. How electric current is propagated along a long wire (about 600 miles long). A voltage is applied to the left-hand end of the wire for $\frac{1}{1000}$th of a second, removed for the next $\frac{1}{1000}$th second, and then applied again for the next $\frac{1}{1000}$th second. At the end of the first period (top of figure), the electronic disturbance has passed along section A of the wire to point P_1, about one third of the length of the wire. During the next period (center) this disturbance continues along section B to point P_2, but since no voltage is then applied no disturbance appears in section A. During the third period (bottom), a new disturbance passes along section A, and the initial disturbance has passed through section C and reached the far end of the wire, at the right.

thousandth of a second at a time. We apply this
to a wire 600 miles or approximately 9×10^5 meters long, and consider the resulting electronic dis-
turbances. At the end of the first thousandth of a
second, just as the voltage is being switched off, the
front of the disturbance will have traveled

$$\frac{3 \times 10^8}{1000}$$

or 3×10^5 meters, and will have reached the point
P_1, a third of the way down the wire. All electrons
in the first third (A) will have been disturbed,
though to different extents. Thus the electron e will
have reached its maximum displacement; the electron e_1 will only just have begun to move. During
the second thousandth of a second, the middle
third of the wire (B) will be disturbed. By the end
of it, e_1 will have completed its displacement and
e_2 will have just started. But no movement of electrons will occur in either A or C. The original disturbance will not yet have reached C, and there is
temporarily no voltage applied at the source to affect A. During the third thousandth of a second,
a new disturbance will begin at the source and
reach P_1 as before. The original disturbance will
traverse C and reach the end of the wire. The middle section will be undisturbed. This is how current
is propagated in a wire.

An alternating voltage is one that is applied first
in one direction and then in the other. This produces an alternating current, in which the electrons
no longer undergo an over-all migration in one direction, but oscillate about a mean position. However, energy is still being expended in overcoming
the resistance of the wire. The number of reversals
per second is called the frequency. The frequency
of the usual power system is 60 cycles per second.

The frequency of the current used on television's Channel 13, however, is around 210 megacycles. This means that the electron flow is alternating 210 million cycles each second! It is only by virtue of their extremely small inertial mass that electrons are able to perform such complicated gyrations and to change direction with this almost inconceivable rapidity.

Currents in Gases and Vacuums

In gases the situation is, if anything, still more complicated. We have already touched on this in connection with the emission of line spectra (page 36), and what follows is to some extent a repetition of what was said there. At atmospheric pressure all gases are bad conductors. Why is this? The first point is that in a gas the atoms or molecules are usually not ionized. There are, therefore, no free electrons, and in order to produce some we must lift them up the full height of the energy well because the atoms or molecules are isolated from their neighbors. Unless we start heating the gas to inconveniently high temperatures, the necessary energy can be provided only by the photoelectric effect or by a voltage applied across electrodes in the gas. Even if a few ions and electrons *are* produced, they will suffer repeated collisions with unionized gas molecules, lose energy, and tend to recombine before they can reach an electrode. To make the current flow more easily through a gas, we must either increase the electric field (a function both of voltage and the shape and separation of the electrodes) or decrease the number of gas molecules present. The first will accelerate the ions more between successive collisions. The second will reduce the frequency of the collisions themselves. Once a current or discharge has started, the positive ions arriving at the negative electrode or *cathode* eject electrons from its surface atoms. These, in their turn, are drawn to the positive electrode or *anode,* along with the other electrons originally derived from the gas atoms. The situation is very complicated, and we shall thankfully pass on to the simpler environment of the vacuum tube.

In a vacuum there is no current carrier available in the medium, since there is no medium. Any charged bodies which are to pass from one electrode to the other will have to be provided by the electrodes themselves. Our knowledge of the atom leaves no possible doubt that it will be far easier to detach an electron than an ion from a metal electrode. Thus, current in a vacuum, as in a metal, is carried exclusively by electrons.

If we now concentrate attention on the surface of a metal electrode in a vacuum tube, we find there are three ways of persuading an electron to leave the comfort and security of its family environment and launch out into space. The first is bombardment with photons (*photoelectric* emission). The second (*field* emission) is to apply a very strong electric field near the surface, so that the electron no longer experiences its normal force of attraction back toward the body of the metal. This may be done by shaping the electrode (for example, in a point so that the exposed electrons are attracted by as few ions as possible) and applying a high positive voltage to a nearby anode (positive electrode). Rather high voltages must be applied to liberate electrons by this method.

The third method is to heat the cathode. By thus increasing the kinetic agitation of the electrons, *thermoelectric* emission is brought about, even without the application of an external electric field. The process is analogous to the evaporation of molecules from the surface of a liquid. In the absence of an externally applied field, a cloud of electrons rapidly accumulates just outside the surface of the cathode. The mutually repelling negative charge of this cloud, known as a *space charge*, prevents further electrons from "boiling off." The situation is similar to the dynamic equilibrium that exists between the molecules above and below the surface of a liquid. Only when a voltage is applied, charging the anode positive compared to the cathode, are the space-charge electrons swept away toward the anode, so allowing the escape process to become continuous (Figure 8). A typical relation

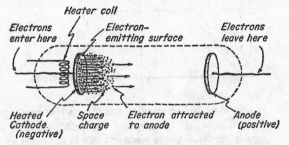

Fig. 8. How current flows through a vacuum tube. When the cathode is heated, some of its electrons become energetic enough to escape from its surface. They form a cloud, or space charge, which inhibits the escape of additional electrons. When a positive voltage is applied to the anode at the other end of the vacuum tube, the free electrons are attracted to it, and this partially removes the space charge and allows more electrons to escape from the cathode. The continual flow of electrons from cathode to anode constitutes the current through the tube.

between current flow and anode voltage is shown in Figure 9.

It should be noted that thermoelectric emission will yield only direct current. If an alternating voltage is applied to the tube, at those times when the heated electrode is the negative cathode it will emit electrons. When the other electrode becomes the cathode, being cold, it will not emit, so the flow of current cannot reverse.

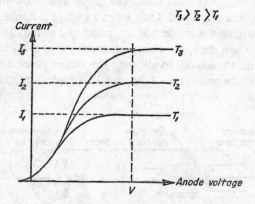

Fig. 9. How temperature affects the current in a vacuum tube. At temperature T_1, sufficient energy is imparted to the electrons within the cathode to allow a given number to escape per second, represented by the current I_1. Anode voltages greater than V cannot force a greater current. At higher temperatures T_2 and T_3, more and more electrons are sufficiently energized to escape, and currents I_2 and I_3, respectively, become possible. In each case when the available escaped electrons are all drawn off, further increases in anode voltage cannot cause a greater current, as the flat plateau on each curve indicates.

Currents and Magnetism

We have now completed our survey of current flow in the three different media and will conclude these preliminaries by touching on the two most important effects of electric current, heat and magnetism.

Heat is one form in which energy is dissipated as a result of the resistance of the medium. We have seen how any electron will alter the electric field surrounding any atom or ion which it passes near. In the most important case, that of a solid, this alters the vibration of the atom or ion and so causes energy to be dissipated throughout the solid. The solid thus gets hotter. The chief practical application of the thermal effect of a current in television is heating the filaments in the many vacuum tubes which are necessary. (But let us not forget the hot filaments in the studio lights!)

The magnetic effect of current is something our untrained instincts grasp much less readily. The facts are briefly these. When a direct and steady

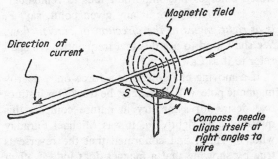

Fig. 10. The magnetic field caused by current in a wire can be detected by the deflection of a nearby compass needle.

current flows along a wire, a nearby compass needle is deflected as in Figure 10. This must mean that a force is acting on the two poles of the needle. This force is magnetic in character. Just as we have introduced the idea of a gravitational and an electric field, so we may plot the intensity and direction of the magnetic forces around a wire in the form of a magnetic field. This is shown in Figure 11, from

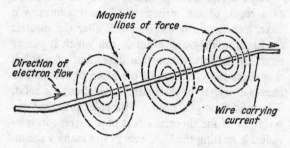

Fig. 11. Lines of force represent the presence of a magnetic field. The direction of the force is always at right angles to the current creating the magnetic field.

which emerges one important fact to remember. This is that the *force* at any given point, say, P, *is at right angles to the direction of current flow.* We shall need to use this fact frequently. We shall refer to it as Law 1.

If a moving charge exerts a force on a nearby magnetic pole, will the reverse be true? Our instinctive desire for symmetry in nature compels this question, and rightly so. It was Michael Faraday who, in 1822, first confirmed that the reverse is true by showing that a magnet does indeed affect nearby moving charges. In fact, it will cause the whole wire carrying the current to move. Let us call this Law 2. You can try for yourself the identical effect a magnet has on a beam of free electrons in a vacuum, by bringing one near to the picture tube of your set.

Having seen the mutual interaction between a magnet and a conductor which is carrying a current, we may now naturally ask what happens when a magnet is brought near a conductor which is not. The answer is that no matter how close the magnet lies, no matter even if the wire is repeatedly coiled around the magnet, no effect is produced. However, immediately the magnet is *moved* in the vicinity of a closed loop of wire, a current is *induced*. This is Law 3. The current continues to flow just so long as the magnet and wire continue to move relative to each other. The faster they move, the larger the induced current.

Now, since we have already seen that a current always "carries around with it" its own magnetic field, we can use a second wire (with a current passing through it) to reproduce the field originally caused by the magnet. The whole situation is summarized in its simplest form in Figure 12. When the wire P carries a steady (so-called *primary*) current, it generates a magnetic field (Law 1). If it is now moved in the vicinity of the wire S, the wire is subject to a varying magnetic field and this induces a (so-called *secondary*) current in it (Law 3). Alternatively, if the two wires are held stationary, the same varying magnetic field may be produced by passing a varying primary current (or alternating current) instead of a steady primary current. The production of an electric current in one conductor by means of a current in another is known as *mutual induction*.

Finally, the direction of the induced secondary current may be deduced from a law discovered by the German physicist H. F. E. Lenz (1804–65). The secondary current, like any other, can be made to do work. Therefore, work must have been done

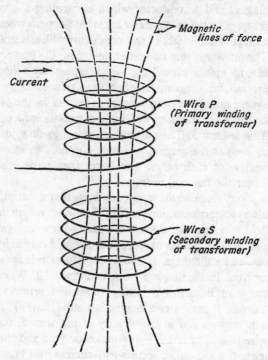

Fig. 12. Induced electric currents. A steady current in the primary winding will cause a current to be induced in the secondary winding only if the two windings are in relative motion. This principle is used in an electric generator. If the two windings are stationary, as in a transformer, a secondary current will be induced only if the primary current is changing. Hence transformers work on alternating (varying) current, not on direct (steady) current.

inducing it. This burden of work must be borne by
the agent responsible for inducing the secondary
current. Consequently, the induced current must be
in such a direction that its magnetic field will inhibit and make more difficult the original action
which produced it. This is Law 4; we shall apply it
to another important case of induction at the end
of this chapter.

So much for the experimental facts of the magnetism resulting from current flow. We can summarize them in terms of electrons. A magnetic field
is produced whenever electrons move in a non-
random fashion. Whether it be in a continuous
stream down a metal rod, or in a continuous stream
through a vacuum (the presence or absence of a
material conductor is irrelevant); whether electrons are circling around a coil of wire or orbiting
around an atomic nucleus—in both cases there is
the same magnetic effect. The magnetic properties
of a bar of iron are, indeed, merely the sum of
those of its constituent atoms. In magnetized iron,
the majority of the electron orbits have become
orientated in the same direction, so that their effects reinforce one another. Magnetism is equally
important whether our unit of scale is that of the
single atom or the whole earth.

Guiding Electrons

Now let us see how some of the things we have
learned about electrons are put to practical use.
There are a number of basic operations we must
be able to perform in order to forge the remaining
links of the television chain. First, we need to be
able to focus and steer a beam of electrons. We
have already hinted how this beam is used to paint

a fluorescent picture on the screen of the receiver, and we shall in fact need a similar beam in the image tube of the camera to "read off" the information from the electronic image (page 45). Next, this electrical information emerges from the camera in the form of a current whose intensity varies sporadically, peaks representing bright points on the image and troughs representing dark. We need to be able to amplify this so-called "picture signal" current to protect its fine details from hazards that will constantly tend to destroy them. Indeed, we shall have to amplify it repeatedly. Amplification means multiplying the flow of electrons without changing the essential pattern. Without it neither radio nor television would be feasible. Third, since (for reasons given later) it is not possible to broadcast the amplified picture signal *by itself,* we need what is called a carrier current, onto the back of which it can be loaded. This carrier is simply an alternating current of very high frequency, but we have to know how to generate it, and how to imprint the pattern of the picture signal onto the carrier frequency. This process, the modulation introduced in Chapter 1, is comparable to writing a letter on blank notepaper before sending it through the mail. Finally, at the receiving end we have two more problems to solve: that of tuning, which ensures that the letter is delivered to the right address; and that of detection, or reading what words are written on the notepaper. This is the reverse of modulation, and consists of disentangling the picture signal from the carrier frequency.

We shall not be able to solve all these problems in this preliminary chapter. In particular, modulation and detection will be left until Chapter 5. But

the others we can make a shot at in the light of
our present knowledge.

First of all, then, how can we focus and steer
a beam of electrons in a vacuum tube? Clearly we
need the equivalent of a system of lenses like that
used to focus the path of light in an optical instrument. Glass lenses are useless, of course; like any
other solid, they would merely halt or scatter the
electrons, with the usual production of heat and
fluorescence. We can, however, use *magnetic*
lenses in an *electron gun* (Figure 13). Next we
must steer the beam. Outside the neck of the vacuum tube, say, the picture tube of the receiver, is
a coil of wire in two parts, one above and one
below (also shown in Figure 13). If a current is
passed through a coil, a magnetic field is generated

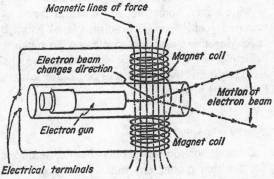

*Fig. 13. How magnetism is used in a television
picture tube. A beam of electrons, formed in an
electron gun, passes through a magnetic field
produced by magnet coils on either side of the
neck of the tube. The electrons are thus forced
to move at right angles to the lines of force, and
the beam is deflected across the viewing screen,
tracing out a line of the image.*

along its axis—that is, across the neck of the tube
(Law 1, page 64). A beam of electrons passing
along the neck, say, on their way to the viewing
screen, will act as an electric current cutting across
the lines of magnetic force, and will therefore be
deflected (Law 2). The direction of deflection
turns out to be at right angles not only to that of
the magnetic field but also to that in which the electrons are themselves traveling. In other words, the
beam will be swept sideways, *and* to an amount
depending on the strength of the current passed
through the deflecting coils. If we arrange a similar
pair of half-coils at right angles to the first, we can
deflect the electron beam "up and down" as well.
By judicious adjustment of the two coil currents
we can combine sideway with up-and-down deflection so that the beam hits any desired spot on the
viewing screen, somewhat as we can arrive at any
required position on a two-dimensional graph by
specifying the x and y co-ordinates. So much, in
principle, for our first problem, though we shall
have to discuss the finer details of picture scanning
in the next chapter.

Amplifying Currents

Second, how do we amplify the picture current
(or for that matter any other varying current)?
Here again we use a vacuum tube, but the geome-
try of the tube (in this form called a radio tube)
is different, though naturally this does not affect
the essential principle of its operation. As shown
in Figure 14, the cathode is now in the center; it
consists of a hollow metal cylinder. Its outer surface is covered with a coating of barium and stron-
tium oxides, which are particularly good electron

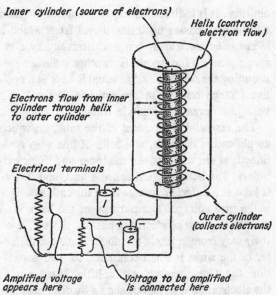

Inner cylinder (source of electrons)

Helix (controls electron flow)

Electrons flow from inner cylinder through helix to outer cylinder

Electrical terminals

Outer cylinder (collects electrons)

Amplified voltage appears here

Voltage to be amplified is connected here

Fig. 14. The essential elements of an electronic vacuum tube ("radio tube"). Battery 1 makes the outer cylinder positive, and, being negatively charged, electrons liberated from the surface of the inner cylinder flow to the outer cylinder. To get to the outer cylinder, they must pass through a helix, a coil of fine wire wound around the inner cylinder. Battery 2 makes the helix negative, and some of the electrons which would otherwise reach the outer cylinder are repelled. If now we connect a varying voltage between the helix and the inner cylinder, an amplified version of this voltage appears between inner and outer cylinders. The wavy lines represent resistors (see Fig. 4). This fundamental amplifying action is the key function of the whole science of electronics.

emitters. It is indirectly heated from a hot tungsten wire, which passes up inside it and from which it is insulated electrically but not thermally by a ceramic sleeve. The anode is another cylinder surrounding the cathode and as usual is kept at a positive voltage relative to the cathode. We call this voltage difference the anode voltage.

The essential component of the tube, on which amplification depends, is a helix of fine wire positioned, as shown, between the inner and outer cylinders. The helix is often called a grid, and it, too, is kept at a different voltage from the cathode. This is the grid voltage. The purpose of the helix is to modify the flow of electrons passing through it on their way from cathode to anode. Since the diameter of the wires is small compared to their separation, the wires themselves offer little obstruction to the electron flow, as can be shown by disconnecting the grid battery. Any obstruction or encouragement the helix supplies to the electron flow is caused by changing the grid voltage. If, for instance, the helix is made negative with respect to the cathode, it clearly will repel the oncoming electrons and tend to drive them back whence they came. Conversely, a positively charged helix will tend to assist the electron flow, by sweeping away electrons from the cathode surface regions toward the anode. But since the grid is much closer to the cathode than is the anode, the effect of its charge will be correspondingly more pronounced. In other words, a given change in grid voltage will have a much greater influence on the electron flow than a similar change in anode voltage. Particularly if the anode voltage is kept constant, the electron flow will exactly mirror any change in grid voltage.

Such an arrangement is called a *triode* vacuum tube, because it has three electrodes.

Now, supposing we take the picture current emerging from the camera and pass it through a resistor. By Ohm's Law this produces a difference in voltage between the ends of the resistor, which therefore becomes the equivalent of a battery. Moreover, the voltage keeps precisely in step with the picture current as the latter varies from instant to instant, and may therefore be termed the *picture voltage*. If this is now applied between the cathode and helix of a triode, the resulting current through the tube is once more an exact image of the picture current. Have we merely made an uninteresting copy of the original? No . . . because the current through the tube, although modified by the picture voltage, is in the first instance supplied by the anode voltage. And the latter may be increased to produce a current which is much larger than the original picture current. We have thus multiplied the electron flow while retaining its essential pattern. In other words, we have amplified it. Once again, it is only because of the very small mass of the electron that the triode can faithfully trace all the variations of signal intensity which occur with almost unbelievable speed. It can easily handle changes every hundred millionth of a second.

An Electronic Pendulum

So much for amplification. Our third problem was to generate the high-frequency alternating current for producing the radio wave. Fortunately, our generator is already at hand—the triode! First, however, let us look at the nature of electrical oscillations in more detail, and introduce the idea that a given circuit may have a "natural frequency" much as a pendulum has. To do this, we must start with the very simple circuit of Figure 15. This contains

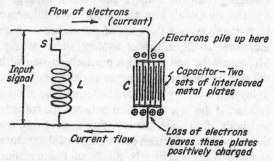

Fig. 15. When a coil and capacitor (condenser) are connected by the switch S, an alternating current flows, as the electrons move through the coil alternately from one set of capacitor plates to the other. The frequency of the alternating current is determined by the inductance L of the coil and the capacity C of the capacitor; it is the frequency at which the inductive and capacitive reactances are equal.

a capacitor C, a coil of wire L, and a switch S. A typical capacitor consists of two sets of conducting plates parallel to each other but separated by layers of insulator, either air or some suitable solid. At all events, electrons cannot flow directly from one set of plates to the other. The first point to note, therefore, is that *direct* current cannot flow through such a capacitor even if there is a suitable voltage source, because the circuit is interrupted by the insulating layers. Electrons would merely build up on one plate of the capacitor until their negative charge repelled any more that were approaching along the wire, the converse occurring on the other plate. The maximum charge Q which can be acquired in this way by a capacitor depends on both the charging voltage V and the so-called *capacity* of the capacitor C. Mathematically $Q = CV$. This is the equation for a capacitor ("capacitor" is the modern term for condenser).

But if a direct current cannot flow, an alternating current can. There is nothing to prevent a crowd of electrons from building up and then dispersing again, on each set of plates in turn. The effect of such a migration would be to set the electrons in the intervening wire and coil scurrying back and forth in an attempt always to be one of the boys. Such a process would be an electrical oscillation and would occur if we started with the plates of the capacitor charged and then closed the switch S. There are of course certain factors that tend to inhibit such frantic social activity. We will take each of them in turn.

First is the resistance of the circuit. Although there is no resistor specifically shown in the diagram, the wires and the coil both have a finite resistance. We have just seen (page 73) that the voltage across any part of this resistance keeps precise step with the current fluctuations according to Ohm's Law. For the moment, however, we may neglect the circuit's resistance except to note that in overcoming it work has to be done, the energy being dissipated as heat. This has the effect of damping the oscillations (Figure 16) unless fresh energy is put into the circuit from an outside source to keep them going.

Second is the capacitor. Strange as it may seem, this also offers opposition to an oscillating current. This may be expressed in terms of a quantity known as the *capacitive reactance* X_c, which oc-

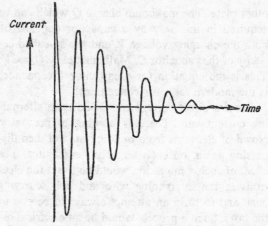

Fig. 16. When the switch of the circuit of Fig. 15 is first closed, the stored charge on the capacitor causes the alternating current to flow vigorously. But with each succeeding oscillation, energy is lost in the form of heat as the current passes through the resistances associated with coil, connecting wire and capacitor. Consequently, the size of the oscillation, as shown here, steadily decreases.

cupies an analogous place to resistance in an Ohm's Law type equation. Thus $V = X_c I$, where V is the voltage drop across the capacitor and I is the current. It can be proved that $X_c = \dfrac{1}{2\pi f C}$; in other words, for a given capacitor the reactance is inversely proportional to the frequency of the current oscillation. A capacitor opposes a lower frequency more than a high.

Third is the coil. We have already discussed the phenomenon of *mutual* inductance between two coils; how a varying current in one produces (via its varying magnetic field) a varying voltage in the other. From here it is a short step to understanding *self*-inductance. The magnetic field of the primary coil cuts across not only the secondary coil but also the primary coil itself. A varying voltage is thus produced in the primary as well as in the secondary —indeed, it is produced even if there is no secondary. Moreover, because the induced voltage always opposes the original agent producing it (Law 4, page 67), it will tend here to oppose the voltage driving the current through the coil. It is for this reason that any coil offers opposition to the passage of an oscillating current, quite independently of its normal *resistance*. This additional opposition is called its *inductive reactance* X_l. Again $V = X_l I$. This time it can be proved that $X_l = 2\pi f L$ where L is a constant of the coil comparable to the capacity of a condenser; or, for a given coil the reactance is directly proportional to the frequency of the current oscillation. A coil opposes a higher frequency more than a low.

The reactances for coil and capacitor are thus seen to work in opposition, in that one increases with frequency and the other decreases. But they are in opposition in more senses than this. It turns out that there is a difference in what is called phase. This is not as alarming as it sounds. Figure 17 shows a plot of the commonest form of current oscillation, the so-called *sine wave*. Both coil and condenser oppose such a current by generating an opposing voltage, the equations for which we have just stated. Apart from their purely numerical values, it can be shown that the voltage across the capacitor, for instance, "lags" behind the current by a quarter of a cycle. Like a perverse student in a ski class, it always turns at a different place from the instructor. If we take any given point in a cycle,

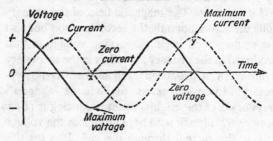

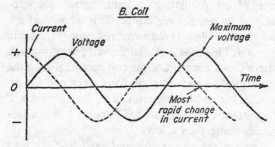

Fig. 17. *When the alternating currents and voltages of an oscillating circuit are plotted against time, they assume the wave shape known as a sine wave. The current through a capacitor is always out of step with the voltage across it, since the current is zero when the capacitor is fully charged, and the current is maximum just when there is equal charge on both sets of plates (zero voltage). In a coil, as shown at the bottom, the self-induced voltage is maximum when the current is changing most rapidly; that is, just as the current is going through zero, so the current and voltage are out of step in this case also. However, the relative timing of current and voltage is just the reverse of the capacitor's.*

it is not hard to see why. At x in Figure 17A, for instance, the current flow is zero and about to reverse its direction. This is just when the capacitor has become fully charged; so the voltage across it is seen to be at a maximum. At y the current is at its greatest, just when the charges have equalized on the condenser's plates; so the voltage is zero.

The case of the coil is the exact reverse. Here the self-induced voltage "leads" the current by an equal amount (Figure 17B). If we combine the two diagrams it will be seen that the two voltages from capacitor and coil tend to oppose each other in a very real sense. Indeed, when they are equal in magnitude, they exactly cancel out. In these circumstances there will be *no* opposition to current oscillation in the circuit (except from the resistance). When are their magnitudes equal? $X_c = \dfrac{1}{2\pi fC}$ and $X_l = 2\pi fL$. Therefore X_c and X_l will be equal when $\dfrac{1}{2\pi fC} = 2\pi fL$, or when $f = \dfrac{1}{2\pi}\sqrt{\dfrac{1}{LC}}$. For a given circuit the current will thus tend to oscillate at this frequency, its so-called natural frequency. This corresponds to the natural period of swing for a pendulum, and mathematicians will note that even the form of the equation is analogous.

Because of air resistance a pendulum will gradually stop swinging unless it is periodically pushed by some external agent. Similarly, circuit resistance will dampen electrical oscillation unless energy is put in from an outside source to replace that lost. But, just as pushing the pendulum at the wrong moment will kill the swing, so electrical oscillations are best perpetuated by feeding in energy with a frequency equal or near to the natural frequency of the circuit. Only then will the circuit "resonate."

Let us now return to the problem of producing alternating current of any required frequency. We need to construct a circuit that will have this as its natural frequency and then feed energy into it from a suitable source. This source, as previously mentioned, can be a triode. In Figure 18 we can

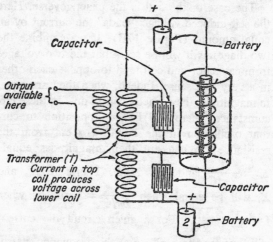

Fig. 18. How a vacuum tube can generate an alternating current. Batteries 1 and 2 serve the same functions as in Fig. 14. Any alternating-current voltage across the lower coil of the transformer is amplified by the tube and appears as a magnified current in the upper coil. This, in turn, reinforces the voltage across the lower coil, and the process repeats itself around the circuit, like a dog chasing its tail. By adjusting the number of turns in the transformer coils or the size of the capacitors, we can produce alternating current of any desired frequency, up to hundreds of millions of cycles per second. The a-c power generated by the circuit is available across the terminals of the third coil.

Plate I. Small picture dots, thousands of them, compose printed pictures and television images, too, as shown in the inset. This scene was taken at a CBS color telecast.

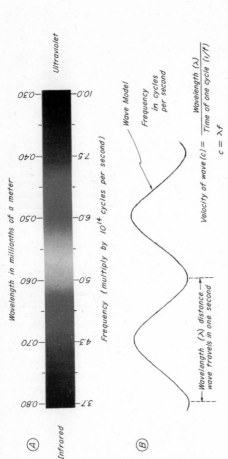

Plate II. The visible spectrum (A), and the frequencies and wave lengths associated with different colors. When light passes through a material like glass, it is slowed down. Its frequency remains the same, but its wave length is decreased in proportion to the change in speed. The diagram (B) shows that the speed of light c is actually the number of wave lengths the light moves forward in a second; that is, it is the product of the wave length λ times the number of cycles per second f (c = λ f).

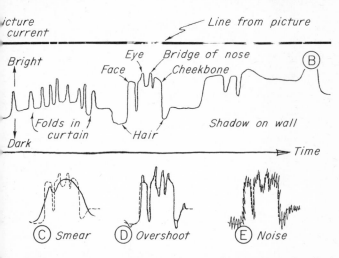

Plate III. A typical television image (A) with strip (scanning line) removed. B shows the strip and the corresponding video waveform. A portion of the waveform, representing the model's face, is repeated in C, D, and E to show the waveform defects of smear, overshoot, and noise.

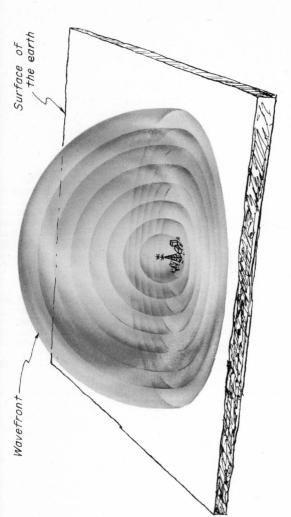

Surface of the earth

Wavefront

Plate IV. As the radio waves leave the transmitting antenna and expand into space, the energy radiated at any instant forms a wave front like the surface of an ever-expanding bubble. The wave becomes rapidly weaker as it travels, since the energy is spread over a larger and larger area.

cause a fluctuating current to flow through the tube by varying the voltage on the grid. We call this voltage the input. We can also draw off an alternating voltage from the circuit by using a secondary coil or transformer T, which we call the output. The output voltage may be large or small, depending on the number of turns in the secondary coil, but its frequency is always equal to that of the main circuit. The only problem is, how can we ensure that the frequency of the input is also equal to that of the output? Why not "feed back" the output into the input? This would automatically solve the problem. In practice if we have a step-up transformer, only a small part of the output need be so used, the rest being available as net output. No energy supply from outside is needed even to start the oscillator, since closing the battery switch or producing any sudden change in the electrical constants of the circuit will start a voltage pulse which rapidly builds up to a steady oscillation. Circuits of this type can be constructed (in various physical forms) to yield frequencies as high as a thousand megacycles and power as great as many thousands of watts.

But the use of the oscillating circuit is not exhausted by this one example; it is only just beginning. Such a circuit is the very basis of tuning. We have just considered a process where we deliberately fed into the circuit a single frequency with which it was designed to resonate. This is the most efficient way of producing oscillations, but it is not the only one. If we expose the circuit to a wide variety of frequencies simultaneously, it will select from them all the one frequency with which it can resonate, with as much discrimination as a gourmet selecting dishes from a tray of hors d'oeuvres. The

setup of Figure 19 shows how energy is fed into
the tuning circuit containing the secondary coil S
by mutual induction from the antenna current arriving in the primary. By changing either the coil
or the condenser we can adjust the resonance of
the circuit to conform to the frequency of the radio
wave we wish to tune in.

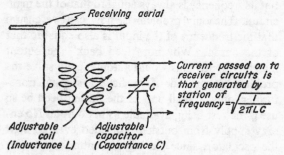

*Fig. 19. How a television set is tuned. Alternating
current flows back and forth between the ends of
the antenna through the primary coil P. By transformer action a similar current is induced in the
secondary coil S, across which is the capacitor
C. By adjusting the condenser or coil, we can
change their reactances until they are exactly
equal at the frequency of the desired station. The
coil and capacitor then form a resonant circuit,
and the current flow is maximum for that station.
Other stations, on different frequencies, produce
comparatively little effect, so the circuit "tunes
in" the desired station and rejects the others.*

In this chapter we have come to know the conduction electron, how it is urged by electrical pressure, or voltage, to move in orderly fashion with
its neighbor electrons and thus become an electric
current. We know how current flowing in an electrical resistance causes heating of the resistance

and how it produces, across the ends of the resistance, a voltage which keeps strict step with any changes in the current. We know that current flow is really a "nudge-thy-neighbor" or buck-passing act, and that the electrons themselves move considerably slower than molasses in January. We have rediscovered the exciting connection between electric current and magnetism and have learned our four laws.

These basic physical tools, of course, are used in all branches of electric science; here we have seen their use in forming and steering electron beams, in amplifying signal currents, in generating alternating currents, and in tuning or selecting one frequency from another. But now we are ready to get back to the main business of this book, how basic physics plays its part in television. Now we can turn in the next chapter to the basic functions of the television camera and the picture tube, by which they encode light (Chapter 2) into electricity (Chapter 3) and decode it back again into light.

CHAPTER 4

Light into Electricity and Back Again

The unique feature of television is the virtually instantaneous conversion of a complicated visual image into an electric current, and vice versa. Apart from these two stages, the rest of the transmission process is very similar (and equally puzzling) to old-fashioned sound radio. It is these terminal stages that we shall consider in detail in this chapter.

Perhaps it is almost too obvious to be worth mentioning that two electric currents mix when they are sent down the same wire, rather as do two liquids poured into the same bottle. All electrons are identical, so that if there are two electron streams representing steady direct currents of, say, 5 amperes and 10 amperes, they will merge into a single current of 15 amperes. When we come to consider currents that are not steady, we find that bursts or *pulses* of electron flow are similarly additive. It is for this reason that it is impossible to transmit all the details of a whole picture simultaneously. Even when we have a device for converting each small individual area of the picture into a pulse of current whose strength matches the respective brightness, if we transmitted all these pulses at the same instant down a single wire, they would merge into one large pulse. The pulses' strength would then be proportional to the total light falling on the picture as a whole. Of course, we could in theory transmit each individual pulse down its own private wire, and it also is true that elaborate electrical circuits can be devised to transmit several currents simulta﹁ ously (in somewhat the same way that more than one radio program can be sent over the air at the same time). But the cost and complexity of either of these solutions are so great that they are not practical for television service.

Telephoto and Motion Pictures

On the other hand, if we feed pulses into the wire one after the other, they emerge at the other end in the same sequence, with their individuality maintained. It would therefore be perfectly possible to send information about the brightness of each small area of the picture in turn, and then put it all together again at the receiving end. This idea will immediately be recognized as closely connected with that of "scanning," briefly mentioned at the end of Chapter 2. Indeed, the electrical transmission of pictures by scanning was tried before the Civil War, and was developed into a practical system when still pictures were sent by radio from London to New York as early as 1924.

In this telephoto system the picture to be transmitted is wrapped around a rotating drum. As the drum turns, a thin pencil of light is focused on it so that it moves slowly along the drum's axis. In this way the pencil "scans" the entire picture surface in spiral fashion. At any instant the light reflected from the drum is proportional to the brightness of that particular part of the picture. This reflected light is then made to fall onto a photocell, which converts it into a picture voltage.

At the receiving end the picture voltage actuates what is known as a modulator glow lamp. This is in essence a simple diode containing a gas, usually helium or neon, at low pressure. A small voltage ionizes some of the gas atoms and excites others (page 34), causing the gas to glow. The brightness of the glow varies widely with small changes of applied voltage, and the tube effectively reconverts the picture voltage into a fluctuating light. The light is focused to a tiny dot on a photographic film, which is wrapped around a rotating drum identical to that of the transmitter. If the two drums are properly synchronized, the dot of light scans the film, exposes it, and reproduces the original picture. The speed of this process is such that it will outpace the carrier pigeon, though not perhaps the jet plane! But, in any case, it is much too slow for television.

In order for a continuous moving picture to be transmitted, the entire scanning process must be completed within the time of persistence of human vision. We saw in Chapter 2 that this means in less than a tenth of a second. Motion pictures are screened at the rate of twenty-four complete pictures every second. In practice it is found more convenient in television to scan the picture slightly faster—thirty times each second. This rate is related to the 60-cycle frequency of the electric power system, a fact which makes possible certain simplifications of receivers, thereby reducing their cost.

The analogy with motion pictures is not complete, however. In movies, twenty-four still pictures are projected one after the other, with intervening periods of darkness to allow the film to be moved to the next frame. In television the scanning process is continuous. By the time the scanner has reached the bottom right-hand corner of the picture the rest of it has already altered. Also, what is known as interlaced scanning is used to reduce flicker still further. The scanning beam scans every other line and transmits a half picture every $\frac{1}{60}$th second. It then returns to fill in the intervening lines and complete the second half picture, the two half pictures being scanned in $\frac{1}{30}$th second.

The total number of picture dots to be scanned is, as we have seen earlier (Chapter 2), quite impressive. The limits of resolution of the human eye necessitate a minimum of about 400 horizontal lines and a corresponding number of vertical divisions. Different countries use different numbers of lines in their television systems. The figures are 525 lines for the United States and elsewhere in North America, 405 for England, 625 in much of Western Europe and Russia, and as high as 819 for France and Belgium.

We shall concentrate for a moment on the 525-line system. When allowances have been made for the fact that some of the lines are hidden behind the mask around the screen, and for the fact that some of the picture details will straddle two lines, a reasonable vertical subdivision of the picture will be into 350 dots. Allowing for the rectangular shape of the picture, we need 460 dots along each horizontal line in order to obtain the same degree of picture *resolution* horizontally as vertically. (This resolution is good enough for viewing at distances of greater than five feet, though inadequate for viewing at reading distance.) Simple multiplication gives us the total number of picture dots that can be laid down on all the lines of the picture as 525×460, or about 240,000. If we now scan the picture thirty times a second, the number of picture dots scanned in that time will be $30 \times 240,000$, or 7.2 million. This is the impressive rate at which the transmission system must convey current pulses. During a one-hour television program our eyes are exposed to several billion changes of light intensity.

We have seen that, by virtue of the small mass of the electrons, electronic circuits can handle even these large numbers of rapid changes with ease. But it should now be obvious why early attempts at mechanical scanning by means of rotating discs were doomed to failure when it came to producing an acceptably detailed picture. Only electrons are fleet-footed enough to deal with such a situation, and commercial television had to await the invention of an electronic scanner.

An Electronic Camera

The problem of image transmission resolves itself into three parts. First (in the camera), we have to see exactly how the number of electrons released from an individual dot can be recorded as a picture voltage. Conversely (in the receiver), we have to examine in detail how the picture voltage can be made to control the intensity of the fluorescence at one particular dot on the screen. Third (in both camera and receiver), we have to arrange for the scanners to follow their tortuous paths across the face of the picture, keeping exactly in step with each other at every instant.

In recording electrically the brightness of our

camera image the first step is to allow the light to fall on a photosensitive (photoelectric-emitting) surface or *photo-cathode*. Electrons are thereby liberated and can be collected by a positively charged anode nearby. The flow of the liberated electrons constitutes a current proportional to the intensity of the light falling on the photosensitive surface. By passing the collected electron current through a resistor, we can create a voltage drop across its terminals. This voltage is proportional to the current strength and gives us the required picture voltage. Unfortunately, however, this voltage is merely a measure of the total number of photoelectrons emitted, that is, the total number of photons hitting the cathode from the whole image at once. From it we can arrive only at the average intensity of the light over the whole image. By contrast, we are interested in measuring the different intensity for each picture dot individually. Clearly some method of insulating each dot from its neighbors must be devised. This insulation can be obtained by forming tiny droplets of the photosensitive silver-cesium compound onto a flat plate of non-conducting mica.

Let us now concentrate on one such droplet—one picture dot. Either we may try to manipulate the photoelectrons emitted from it, or we may take advantage of the fact that a corresponding number of metal atoms will be left positively ionized within each droplet. Both ideas look equally promising; the second was the one employed in the first successful type of electronic camera, V. K. Zworykin's *iconoscope*.

In theory we could conceive of having a separate wire leading to each individual droplet, along which electrons could flow to reconvert the cesium and silver ions into atoms. In practice the tiny size of the droplets makes this obviously impossible. Yet if we join them all together to one wire, we are back where we started, with only an average over-all picture current. This apparent impasse is overcome by the arrangement of Figure 20. On the back

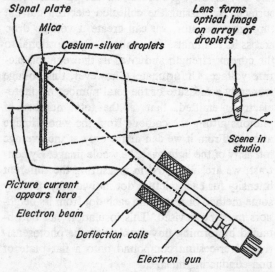

Fig. 20. Zworykin's iconoscope, the first practical television camera tube. The televised scene is focused on a flat mica plate, which is covered with tiny droplets of photosensitive cesium-silver. These emit photoelectrons, and an electrical image is formed. The electron beam, from the sidearm of the tube, scans the electrical image, and as it passes over each droplet, restores it to electrical equilibrium. The change in charge thereby produced on each droplet induces a current in the metallic coating ("signal plate") on the back of the mica, and this changing "picture current" represents the lights and shadows along each line in the picture.

side of the mica dielectric is a thin metal coating, called the signal plate. In effect, therefore, each droplet becomes one plate of a tiny condenser, the other plate, the signal plate, being common to all. When photoelectrons are emitted by our selected droplet, a corresponding number of atoms is left ionized. This will induce a proportional negative charge in the signal plate. But we are not out of the woods yet, for all the other droplets are also doing the same thing, so that the total charge on the common signal plate will be the sum of the individually induced charges and once again will give us only a measure of the average light intensity.

Let us assume that this remains constant for $\frac{1}{30}$th of a second, the time chosen for one complete scanning of the picture. If we could devise some method of discharging the ionized atoms in our one droplet, we would diminish the induced charge on the signal plate by the same amount. Passing to the next droplet, we would discharge its ions and diminish the charge on the signal plate that amount. During the whole $\frac{1}{30}$th of a second, therefore, the induced charge on the signal plate would decrease by a series of steps (Figure 21A). Moreover, since the signal plate is all the time being exposed to constant illumination, the discharged dots lying in the wake, along each scanned line, are being recharged at a constant rate. This has the effect of making the total charge on the signal plate vary about an average value (Figure 21B).

The discharging of the dots is achieved by bombarding them with a pencil of electrons from an electron gun arranged as in Figure 20. The beam scans along a line, passing over the dots on that line in quick succession, and then quickly returns and passes back again over the next line, and so on. By connecting the signal plate through a resis-

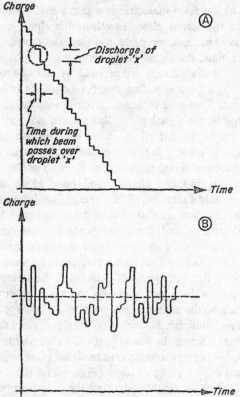

Fig. 21. *The induced electric charge on the signal plate of the iconoscope is changed in two ways: by the successive discharge of the droplets as they are scanned by the electron beam and by the continual charging of all the droplets by the light falling on them from the scene. The discharge effect is shown at A, the sum of the two effects in B. The latter shows that the charge on the signal plate varies about an average value, the changes from the average representing the lights and shadows successively scanned in each line of the image.*

tor to the circuit, we obtain a voltage across the resistor that will be a copy of Figure 21B. If we now pass on to the next $\frac{1}{30}$th second and assume that the general level of illumination has by then changed to some new value, we shall get the same rapid dot-to-dot variations during the repeat of the scanning process, but these variations will be around a new mean (Figure 22). Of course, the general illumination does not vary in this sudden step-wise fashion, but it is still generally true that we can view the picture voltage as undergoing two separate kinds of variation: first, a slow fluctuation depending on major changes in the over-all background or average illumination of the image being televised; and second, very much more rapid fluctuations from successive scanning of the dots. Shortly, we shall see how, in order to *synchronize* the scanning action of the electron beams in both camera and picture tube, it will be necessary to superimpose yet a third type of fluctuations on the picture voltage, the so-called sync pulses. How these three different components are separated or selectively eliminated, we shall postpone until the next chapter.

An Improved Camera: Image Orthicon

Meanwhile, we may now look at a second type of television camera, which is generally superior to the iconoscope and works on somewhat different principles. There are two serious shortcomings of the iconoscope: first, the beam from the scanning gun causes a scattering of surplus electrons, which we have thus far ignored; these fall on other droplets and knock other electrons out of atoms not previously ionized. Since it does not matter *how* the

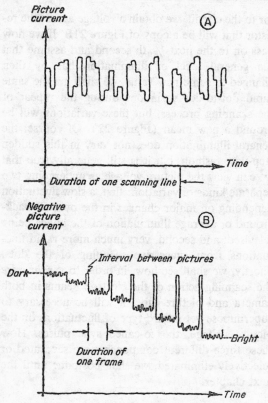

Fig. 22. *The picture current has two kinds of variation: one is the rapid dot-to-dot change representing the fine details of the picture, shown at A. The other is a much slower variation that represents changes in the over-all brightness of the image, shown by the gradual brightening of the picture as a whole at B. The rapid change takes place in a millionth of a second or less; the slow change may take several seconds. In transmitting the picture current, therefore, we must use circuits that will operate fast or slow with equal facility.*

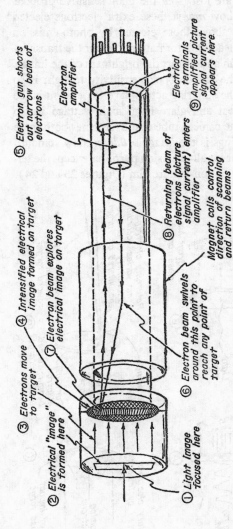

⑤ Electron gun shoots out narrow beam of electrons

Electron amplifier

Electrical terminals

⑨ Amplified picture signal current appears here.

⑧ Returning beam of electrons (picture signal current) enters amplifier

④ Intensified electrical image formed on target

⑦ Electron beam explores electrical image on target

③ Electrons move to target

Magnet coils control direction of scanning and return beams

② Electrical "image" is formed here

⑥ Electron beam swivels around this point to reach any point of target

① Light image focused here

Fig. 23. The image orthicon, the television camera tube used for nearly all studio and outside broadcasts. To see how it operates, follow the numbers. This remarkable electronic device is one of the most sensitive optical devices known to science.

electrons are lost from the photosensitive droplets but only how *many*, these extra electrons ejected over and above those ejected by photo-emission cause misleading information to enter the transmission system and distort the brightness of the image. Second, the iconoscope's sensitivity to light is so low that the suffering actors have to perform in the intense heat and glare from high wattage studio lamps. The camera tube that overcomes both these shortcomings is the *image orthicon*, now standard equipment for all television purposes except the televising of motion-picture film (Figures 23 and 24).

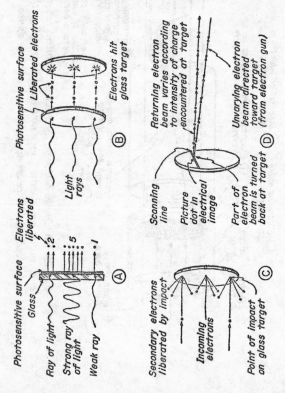

In the image orthicon let us first concentrate on the photoelectrons. Light is made to fall on a photo-cathode as before, but this now is semi-transparent. The cesium-silver compound has been sprayed on its inner surface so that the photo-electrons are ejected away from the source of light and into the heart of the camera. Free electrons tend to emerge from a metal at right angles to its surface. Consequently, these electrons streaming from the photo-cathode preserve the pattern of the image as they travel through space. As one runner takes over from another in a relay race, the electrons temporarily take over carrying the image from the photons which ejected them.

The next take-over occurs when the scurrying photoelectrons are intercepted by the *target,* a very thin glass plate, roughly .0001 of an inch thick (which means that nearly fifty would be needed to make a stack as thick as the paper on which these words are printed). When the photoelectrons hit the glass, they knock out other electrons—*second-*

Fig. 24. (*Opposite*) *Electronic adventures in the image orthicon: A, the incoming light rays liberate photoelectrons from the photosensitive surface. B, the electrons hit the glass target. C, at the target each incoming electron causes several other "secondary" electrons to leave the target, thus increasing the positive charge at each point on the target and intensifying the electrical image. D, still other electrons from the gun explore the rear side of the target, scanning the electrical image line by line. Some of the beam electrons are turned around at the target; the number returning depends on the positive charge encountered at each point in the electrical image. The return beam is the picture current.*

ary electrons—from the glass atoms. Because the photoelectrons have been accelerated by an external voltage during their journey to the glass target, each photoelectron arrives there with enough energy to knock out not one but several secondary electrons. In this way the quantity of usable electrons is multiplied (which in the language of photography corresponds to increasing the "film speed" of the camera tube to ASA 1000 or higher). Their mission accomplished, the secondary electrons are then swept out of the way by a grid of very fine mesh which has a small positive charge relative to the glass.

We can now forget about the secondary electrons and concentrate on the *ionic image* which they have left etched on the glass. Since the glass is very thin, this charge image passes through the glass by electric conduction and is therefore available on the back side of the target. This is like the image left on the cesium droplets of the iconoscope's photo-cathode, and is similarly preserved by virtue of the fact that glass is a good insulator across its surface. The charge image is now scanned, as in the iconoscope, by a beam from an electron gun situated on the far side of the target at the back of the camera tube. Beyond this, all is different from the iconoscope. For in the image-orthicon tube the electron beam is of low velocity. The gun electrons are slowed down by an electrostatic field as they approach the glass so that, when no picture is being televised, they just fail to reach it. They are then accelerated by the same field back toward the gun, but are intercepted and collected by an anode.

When a picture is being televised, however, those points on the glass target which have been

left with a positive charge will snatch electrons
from the scanning beam as it passes over them. The
"dark" parts of the image, with no positive charge,
will not. The intensity of the gun beam returning
to the anode will therefore be continuously altered,
or modulated, by the target's ionic image, which it
has scanned, and the varying current collected by
the anode provides us with the picture signal in
the usual way. No condenser action is involved,
as it is with the iconoscope. The atoms of the
glass target are merely deionized by the electrons
of the beam and are immediately ready to accept
a new positive charge image. This collects electrons, as before, on the next passage of the scanning beam.

The Receiver: Brightness and Contrast

So much for the camera; now for the receiver.
How does it re-create a dot of light of appropriate
brightness from the information of the picture voltage? In the last chapter we examined the function
of an electron gun, and in the chapter before that
we saw that, in the receiver, the thermoelectrons
from a gun are made to cause fluorescence. The
intensity of the fluorescent light emitted by the target screen is proportional to the number of electrons bombarding it; so wherever we want a bright
spot on the picture image we merely make the electron beam more intense as it scans that particular
point. Clearly, then, we need to make the picture
voltage modulate the intensity of the electron beam.
This intensity depends on the voltage difference between cathode and anode, but it is still more sensitive to that between cathode and grid, as in the case
of a triode (page 72). The best way, therefore, to
modulate the intensity of the electron beam is to

apply the picture voltage direct to a control aperture just in front of the hot cathode, before the beam passes through the cylindrical anodes, which also act as focusing lenses (Figure 25).

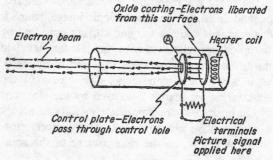

Fig. 25. *An electron gun used in a picture tube. The number of electrons passing through the hole A is determined by the picture voltage. All the electrons that get through are focused so that they land at a point on the viewing screen, where they produce a spot of light.*

As well as receiving the picture voltage, the grid receives an additional adjustable negative voltage called the "bias voltage." Its purpose is as follows: The bias acts as a throttle or valve controlling the beam, and is opened and closed by means of the *brightness* control on the front of the set. In a typical set a negative bias voltage of around 60 volts is enough to repel *all* the thermoelectrons and send them back to the cathode—that is, to shut the valve completely. The screen is then entirely dark. By turning the brightness control to the left, you increase the adjustable bias to such an extent that even the peaks of the superimposed video voltage (Figure 26) do not force electrons through the valve, and so light up the screen. Conversely, by

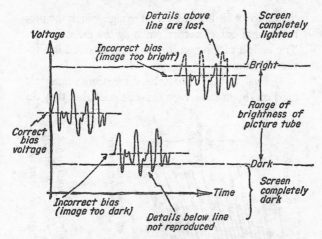

Fig. 26. Two voltages are applied to the picture tube electron gun. The picture voltage which represents the picture content is superimposed, as shown above, on a steady bias voltage supplied by the brightness control of the receiver. By adjusting this bias voltage, we set the over-all brightness of the viewing screen.

turning the knob to the right, you decrease the bias until so many electrons are pouring through the valve that all parts of the screen are bright even when the picture voltage is trying to cut down the intensity. Thus the brightness control, via the negative grid bias, influences the over-all brightness of the whole image. At an intermediate setting of the brightness control, the variations of the picture voltage cause the brightnesses of the picture dots to vary about the average set by the control.

But we are also interested in controlling *contrast* of intensity. This means increasing the difference between the positive and negative peaks of the picture signal—amplifying it. The contrast knob is linked to an amplifying tube through which the picture signal passes before reaching the picture tube. The action of the picture tube is illustrated in Figures 27 and 28.

A final point is that the fluorescent materials used on the target screen must be such that they do

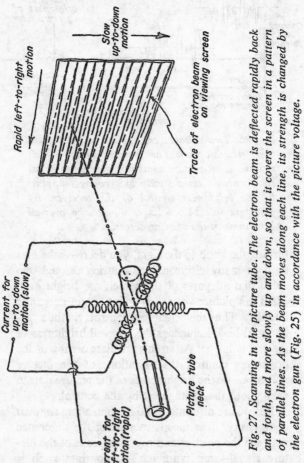

Fig. 27. Scanning in the picture tube. The electron beam is deflected rapidly back and forth, and more slowly up and down, so that it covers the screen in a pattern of parallel lines. As the beam moves along each line, its strength is changed by the electron gun (Fig. 25) in accordance with the picture voltage.

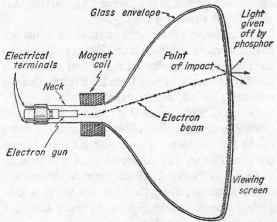

Fig. 28. The final energy transformation of the television system, from electricity to light, occurs just inside the glass face of the picture tube. Here the electron beam hits the phosphor, which transforms kinetic energy into visible radiant energy. As the beam moves, it traces out the lights and shadows of the picture, one line at a time.

not glow for much longer than $\frac{1}{60}$th second after their atoms are hit by the gun electrons; otherwise, they will still be glowing when they are next scanned and this will tend to smear the picture.

Synchronizing the Camera and Receiver

The third and last problem to be solved in this chapter is how to cause the electron beams in both camera and receiver to trace out their complicated scanning paths, and to do so in precise step. We have already seen in principle how these beams may be deflected by a magnetic field applied across the neck of the tube. Now comes the more detailed question of how to give appropriately varying currents to the deflecting coils.

Let us suppose that the beam first falls at the top left-hand corner of the picture. We need to impose on it two separate deflections. The first will draw it steadily across the picture from left to right, thereby scanning one line, and then allow it to jump rapidly back again. Superimposed on this, a second and much slower deflection will draw it steadily down to the bottom of the picture and then let it jump back to the top. The combined trace will then be as shown in Figure 27. Both these deflections are of the same general pattern, which when plotted against time looks like Figure 29. Since deflection

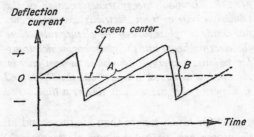

Fig. 29. The current in the magnetic deflection coils must vary in the "saw-tooth" fashion shown here. The steady increase of current marked A causes the electron beam to move at constant speed across the screen. The more rapid decrease marked B brings the beam back to its starting point as rapidly as possible.

is proportional to the current applied to the deflecting coils, this is also the shape of the required current trace. To see how we can manufacture this so-called "saw-tooth" current will require something of a digression.

First, we recognize that the deflecting coils possess the electrical property of self-inductance (page 65, Chapter 3), since the magnetic lines of force link the turns of the coils themselves. The self-induction causes a voltage to appear across the coil which opposes the voltage applied to it, and the opposition is the more vigorous the more rapidly we try to increase the current in the coil. Hence, no matter how fast we increase the voltage applied to the deflecting coil, the current increases more slowly. To produce a saw-tooth current which steadily increases in one direction and then rapidly decreases in the opposite direction, we must apply two very sudden surges of voltage in the respective directions. These are illustrated in Figure 30. At the beginning of the left-to-right scanning motion, a sudden, almost instantaneous, increase in voltage (marked A) occurs, and the voltage thereafter remains constant during the scanning motion. The current produced by this voltage steadily increases. At the end of the scanning line sudden voltage (marked B) is applied in the reverse direction. This surge is much larger than surge A and hence causes the current to decrease faster, deflecting the beam rapidly from right to left back to its starting point. To cause the motions to occur at the required speed (the beam takes about 60 millionths of a second to go from left to right and 5 millionths of a second to retrace) the over-all voltage surges across the coils must attain an over-all value of several thousand volts.

The sudden voltage surges are produced by a vacuum tube (the horizontal deflection tube) which acts as a fast-acting switch. It suddenly connects the deflecting coils to the direct-current power supply of the receiver at time A, and then suddenly

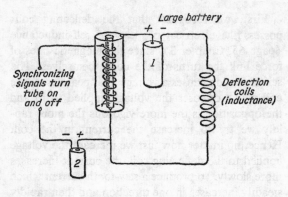

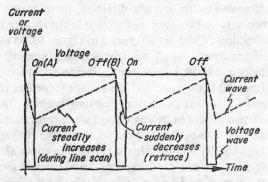

Fig. 30. The saw-tooth-shaped waves of current (Fig. 29) are forced to pass through the deflection coils by a vacuum tube acting as a fast-acting switch which suddenly connects the coils to a source of voltage. Since the coils possess self-inductance, the voltage and current waves have the quite different shapes shown.

disconnects, at time B (Figure 30). Incidentally, the voltage surges across the deflecting coils serve an additional purpose; they are passed through a step-up transformer and then through a diode "rectifier" tube which converts the surges into direct current, at 15,000 to 20,000 volts. This voltage is applied to the picture tube, where it accelerates the beam electrons from the gun to the screen.

A similar process creates the saw-tooth current in the other set of deflecting coils for the up-and-down motion of the beam. Here, however, the motion is very much slower (about 15,000 millionths of a second for the downward motion, 1500 for the upward motion). So smaller and less sudden voltage surges suffice. In fact, the voltage wave more nearly matches the required current wave, as shown in Figure 30. This means that the up-and-down coils possess less self-inductance and more resistance than the left-to-right coils.

Although we have now devised means to make the scanning beam follow the correct trace, there are still two essential details to be cleared up. First, it is obvious that, even though the beam moves extremely fast when traveling back from the end of one scanning line to the start of the next, this part of its journey, known as the retrace, must not produce any visible light. In other words, the gun must be shut off for this period; otherwise, the image will be interfered with. To achieve this a so-called "blanking pulse" is superimposed on the picture voltage by the transmitter at the end of each horizontal line—that is, at a frequency of 15,750. When the picture voltage arrives on the grid of the picture tube, it has to be in its positive phase so that voltage peaks increase the electron flow past the grid and make the picture brighter. When each blanking pulse arrives, it represents a deep trough in the positive phase (Figure 31), and so slams the grid valve tight shut, thereby completely suppressing light on the screen during the retrace.

Superimposed on the blanking pulse is the syn-

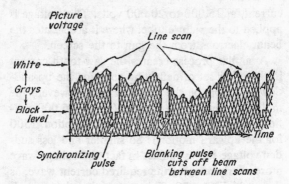

Fig. 31. The picture voltage representing three successive scanning lines. Between the lines, a deep trough A, blanks off the beam while it retraces to the start of the next line. During this portion of the wave, an additional synchronizing pulse is also added. This pulse causes the scanning beam to start its retrace at the proper time.

chronizing pulse (Figure 31). This is abstracted from the picture voltage by a tube known as the clipper, and applied to the circuit which ultimately generates the saw-tooth deflection current. The scanning beam is, thereby, forcibly yanked back to the start of another line at the proper time, irrespective of whether it was ahead of, behind, or right on schedule. In this way the scanner in the receiver is forced to toe the line to the scanner in the camera. The vertical retrace of the scanning beam is blanked out and synchronized in an exactly similar fashion. The vertical pulses come at the end of each 262½ lines (for interlaced scanning) and are disentangled and applied as before.

In practice the method of synchronization must not be easily disaffected by "static," a hazard which so far has not received much mention but which will assume its true importance in the next chapter. Any strong burst of static, sudden increase in signal voltage, would do the job of the sync pulse for it. In this case, the scanning beam would jump back to the left side of the screen prematurely, thereby tearing away part of the picture. For this reason, more complicated circuits have been designed which automatically control the frequency of the horizontal saw-tooth oscillator from the sync pulses. Synchronization is, of course, adjusted by means of the knobs on some sets marked *horizontal hold* and *vertical hold*.

Now at last, we have both our camera and picture ready to work, at least as far as black-and-white pictures are concerned. We can produce a picture voltage which faithfully reproduces the detailed light and shade of the complicated scene that is to be televised. We know that this voltage must be labeled both with blanking and sync pulses to control the horizontal and vertical scanning mechanisms. We can design a picture tube that will respond to the stimulations of the incoming signal with delicacy and faithfulness. All that is now necessary is to transport the picture signal from studio to living room. This is merely one example of transfer of energy, and in the coming chapter we shall once again try to reduce it to a matter of electrons, photons, and waves.

CHAPTER 5

From Studio to Living Room

On its all but incredible journey from the television camera to the viewing screen the picture signal must satisfy the criteria we developed in Chapter 1 for any successful communications system. You will remember that these concern the elements of *speed, accuracy, distortion,* and *power.* In this chapter we shall apply the criteria to *radio waves* and see by what means we can maneuver them into meeting all the demands or, perhaps it would be better to say, bolster them against falling short.

First, it is clear that the television camera establishes the *speed* and *accuracy* of television communications. The camera scans the whole picture 30 times a second; it scans each line in about 50 millionths of a second; it recognizes as many as 7 million changes in light intensity every second. At this tremendous pace it manages to divide each picture into some 200,000 picture dots and to do it with enough accuracy to place each dot in its proper position among tens of thousands of others and to specify the brightness within a few per cent of its original value in the studio image.

The quality of the picture you see in your home can never be better than the camera that scanned it. But, unless we carefully protect it on its journey, it can be very much worse. This is where *distortion* and *power* come in. We must safeguard the picture signal against distortion, and we must keep it powerful enough to overcome, at every stage in the journey, any interference with picture content.

We can make these generalities more specific if we graphically examine (Plate III) the picture-signal wave the camera generates. Here we have selected a typical line from a typical picture and translated the light values along it into the corresponding current values, plotted against time. Such a graph is called the "video waveform." In it we embody all the essentials of the picture to be reproduced in the living room; the task of the television system is to deliver to the picture tube, as faithfully as possible, an electric current having this waveform.

Smear, Overshoot, and Snow

Plate III illustrates several misadventures that may befall the video waveform on its journey. The first (Plate III C) is a form of distortion known as *smear*, which affects the steeper slopes of the wave; before the wave has reached the picture tube, the steepness has decreased. Now, for example, this steep slope may represent a sharp boundary between a ravishing brunette in a black dress and her lighter background. After the distortion the reproduced boundary is comparatively indistinct—the picture looks smeared. Smear occurs whenever the amplifiers (or any other part of the transmission system) fail to operate fast enough to follow the steep slopes the camera generates.

Another form of distortion, known as *overshoot,* occurs if we are too careful to make the amplifiers fast-acting. Then, in its eagerness to follow the steep slope, the amplifier may persist after the original slope is finished; it recovers itself a bit too late. These variations in the waveform (Plate III D) cause unwanted sharp boundaries in the reproduced picture—outlines not present in the original image. You probably can produce smear and overshoot distortions on your own screen if you turn the fine tuning control to either side of the position where you are getting the best reception.

The most general hazard to a successful trip for the video waveform is the presence everywhere in the transmission system of *random currents.* What happens when the picture signal becomes too weak to overcome them is illustrated in Plate III E. Known as *noise* (a term borrowed from sound reproduction), the random currents are caused by the helter-skelter dance of individual electrons moving about in response to thermal forces (Chapter 3). The currents are very small, on the order of a billionth of an ampere, but they are troublemakers because they are entirely random in form and tend to obscure, or at least degrade, the highly detailed and orderly picture current we want to transmit.

This is where the *power* criterion becomes important. When we send a picture current over a wire, or a picture radio wave over the air, the signal weakens steadily as it travels. If we let the signal travel too far without amplification, the picture current will fall to a few billionths of an ampere. Then the picture waveform (Plate III E) becomes inextricably mixed with the equally strong waveforms of random noise currents.

The pictorial result of this misadventure is *snow* —the tiny specks, some bright, some dark, that obscure the picture's fine details. And at this stage, alas, there is nothing whatever we can do about it. The noise has got into the picture, and since noise currents are completely random, there is no systematic way to get them out. Most television viewers are all too familiar with the noise distortion. When you try to tune in a station fifty to a hundred miles away, the signal has become so weak in reaching your antenna that noise predominates. Or if the lead-in wire from the antenna has become disconnected, the wave from even a nearby station becomes too weak to contend with noise generated within the receiver circuits themselves. Try disconnecting the antenna from your own set to check this. The specks on the screen are direct evidence of the random motions of electrons in the receiver circuits.

So, it is evident that if we are to avoid noise interference, we must keep the picture current and radio wave strong. The only way to do this is to insert amplifiers at regular intervals along the pathway of circuits and networks from studio to transmitter. The amplifiers, periodically rejuvenating the signal, must keep the level of its electrical power at least a thousand times as high as the power of the noise currents.

After the transmitter has propagated the radio wave into space, we cannot use more amplifiers, of course; we have lost control. So we must make the transmitter very powerful, and we must erect the transmitting antenna on a high tower or hilltop if the wave is to clear obstructions. And at the receiving end, if we wish to see pictures from distant stations, we must have as tall a receiving antenna as possible and use a receiver designed to keep its internal noise currents within strict bounds. But even when we have taken all these precautions, noise remains the nemesis of the signal. Not only does it limit the range at which we can pick up the signal; the retribution it exacts from signal waves is final: once into the picture, snow cannot be ousted.

The Signal in the Set

Now let us look at the simplest television system, in which radio waves are not used. The block diagram in Figure 32 represents its essential components. The camera and synchronization generator, which we met in the preceding chapter, produce the picture signal, including (Figure 31) the blanking and synchronizing pulses. The picture signal travels along a cable to the receiver. In the course of the journey the orderly electron motions of the signal current gradually weaken as the electrons collide with the metal ions of the cable wires. If the cable is longer than a mile or two, there must be amplifiers to offset the weakening process and keep the strength of the signal above the level of the noise currents. Under these conditions the signal will reach the end of a cable in a reasonable state of preservation, uncontaminated by noticeable noise and, we hope, free of smear and overshoot.

At the receiving end of the cable, the picture signal is separated into the two parts which carry respectively the synchronizing and picture information. We note in Fig. 31 that these two types of information occur on either side of the blanking level of the wave, the sync information below and

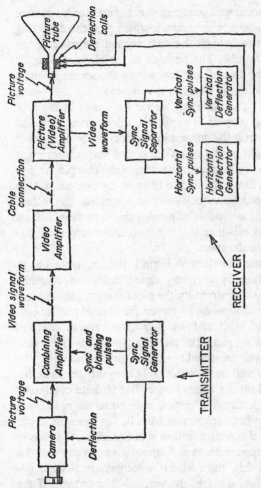

Fig. 32. Elements of a simple closed-circuit television system, in which radio waves are not used, are represented in this block diagram.

the picture information above. By passing the signal through a special form of amplifier (sync separation amplifier) that responds only to the parts of the signal below the blanking level, we separate the sync information from the picture information.

The separated sync pulses are then used to control the deflection generators, which pass the deflecting currents through the coils around the neck of the picture tube. The position of the electron beam is thereby forced to move across the screen in strict step with the beam in the camera.

The picture signal, as we have seen in the preceding chapter, is applied to the electron gun, and it controls the current in the electron beam, so that the light produced on the screen varies from point to point along each scanning line. The picture signal is first amplified to increase its over-all voltage to about 60 volts. When so magnified, the picture voltage is capable of turning the beam from full on to full off—that is, from maximum screen brightness to darkness.

When the electron beam is thus controlled as to direction by correctly timed deflection currents, and as to current by the picture signal, the picture tube produces on its screen the desired picture pattern of lights and shadows. If the synchronization is precise, and if the picture signal has been reasonably well protected against distortion and noise, the image will be an acceptable copy of the scene focused on the camera tube. But if these conditions are not met, the picture may be so degraded that we get little enjoyment from it. For example, if the vertical synchronization is out of kilter, the picture will appear to "roll" upward or downward. To avoid this, the vertical deflection circuits are adjusted by a knob, the vertical-hold control. If the horizontal deflection is out of step, the picture breaks up into parallel jagged bars; this is controlled by the horizontal-hold knob. Finally, the over-all voltage of the picture signal, as applied to the picture tube, may be too great or too small. If it is too great, the highlights of the picture will be too bright and all the dark grays will turn out black. If the voltage is too small, all the tones of the picture are gray, and the picture appears "washed out." To control this, a "contrast control" is provided. This changes the amplification of the picture signal and allows the viewer to adjust the range between black and white to suit his preference. These circuit functions and controls are, of course, common to all picture tubes, wherever used—in a monitor in the studio, in the reproducer unit of a closed-circuit TV system, or in a home receiver.

The Transmitted Wave

Having examined the functions of this non-radio television system, we must now take up the most mysterious part of the journey from studio to living room—the passage of the signal through space. We have already hinted, in Chapter 3, that a steady stream of radio waves is generated by passing a very rapidly alternating current through the transmitting antenna. We know how to generate such a current in a vacuum-tube oscillator (page 80), and we realize that current in the antenna is really a surging back and forth of electrons through the metal conductor of the antenna itself. But in what manner does this current produce a radio wave? And, for that matter, what is a radio wave?

We know that radio waves and light waves are the same thing, except that the wave length in radio is enormously greater than in light. Does this mean that radio waves are really very long-wave photons? This is indeed one way of looking at it. But we must be careful in comparing radio waves with the photon emission we studied in Chapter 2. In a radio antenna we are dealing with millions upon trillions of free electrons moving together. Since these electrons are not bound to atoms, their energies are not fixed at discretely specified, or quantized, levels. Hence the energy radiated by an antenna can have frequencies far lower than those associated with the quantum jumps of bound electrons. The frequency of the radiated energy is, in fact, the frequency of the alternating current sent up into the antenna.

To understand the production of radio waves, we will do well to return to the statement from classical physics which appears on page 38 in Chapter 2: whenever a free electron is accelerated or decelerated, radiation is emitted. Initially, before the transmitter is turned on, the free electrons in the antenna have no orderly motion. Then we turn on the power, and the first cycle of high-frequency alternating current starts. The electrons are then pushed in one direction, say, to the right. In imparting this orderly motion, the transmitter accelerates the electrons from rest to a definite velocity. A fraction of a second later (less than a hundredth of a millionth of a second for a 100-megacycle wave) the electrical pressure from the transmitter reverses, and the electrons are urged to the left. In the process of reversing their motion, the electrons must decelerate to a stop and then accelerate again in the opposite direction. Thus for every cycle of the antenna current there are two accelerations and decelerations of free electrons and a corresponding emission of electromagnetic stresses alternately released into space. Each pair of alternate stresses is a single complete radio wave which moves outward as radiant energy, making room for the endless stream of others that follow.

We can look at it in still another way. We learned in Chapter 3 (page 77) that a current in a coil of wire produces magnetic lines of force which link the turns of the coil and that a changing magnetic field induces a current in the coil. When we pass an alternating current through the coil, the changes in the current produce a changing magnetic field and the changing field in turn induces a current which opposes the original current. We find then that a coil, even if it has negligible electrical resistance, will oppose the flow of alternating current. The opposition is called inductive reactance.

When we pass alternating current through the transmitting antenna, the same thing happens, but with one important difference. The magnetic field which immediately surrounds the antenna induces an opposing current. But the magnetic field at points more remote from the antenna, at distances greater than a few wave lengths of the radio wave, cannot induce an opposition current. Instead, the energy of this remote field becomes permanently detached from the antenna system and flows outward through space. A similar action occurs in the electric field which surrounds the antenna. The electric-field energy from nearby points re-enters the antenna, producing the effect we described (page 75, Chapter 3) as capacitive reactance, while the energy at more remote points becomes detached and flows away.

If we insist, we may oversimplify the situation by noting that it takes time for the magnetic and electric fields to build up at the remote points and time for their respective energies to re-enter the antenna. While the energy reaches and returns from the remote point, the high-frequency current in the antenna reverses, the induced currents are then no longer in opposition, and the inductive and capacitive reactance effects cannot occur. Rather, the effect is like that of a resistance, and this resistance represents an element in which energy is dissipated —the energy of the outgoing radio wave.

These curious effects can be predicted by mathematical manipulation of the basic equations (first formulated by Maxwell) which describe the joint presence of magnetic and electric fields; they are admittedly very difficult to understand in terms of a physical model. Suffice it to say that when alternating current of the proper frequency is passed through an antenna, it appears to encounter a resistance which is entirely unexplained by the electronic and ionic collisions within the antenna itself. This resistance consumes energy which does not appear as heat in the antenna; it appears in space as the energy of the radio wave. In a properly designed antenna, in fact, the ordinary electron-ion collision resistance is very small, and nearly all the transmitter power goes directly into producing the radio wave.

Whatever the mechanism of radio-wave generation may be, we can accept that the radio wave exists, because we can measure its effects—we can pick it up on a receiving antenna at a great distance. Let us now consider what happens to the wave as it passes through space from transmitter to receiver. As the energy flows outward from the antenna, it fills a larger and larger volume of space. We may visualize a single wave as a half of a soap bubble (Plate IV) of ever increasing size. Near the transmitter the surface area of the bubble is small, and the energy contained within each square foot of its surface is large. At greater distances the energy is spread over a much larger area, and the energy within each square foot is correspondingly smaller.

Since the surface of the bubble increases with the square of its radius, the energy per square foot decreases (by virtue of the geometric "dilution") as the square of the distance from the transmitting antenna. Actually, the effectiveness of the energy of the wave diminishes even more rapidly, because part of the wave hits the surface of the earth and is reflected with a *change of polarity*. (Change in polarity might be explained as a reversal of the normal directions of the electromagnetic stresses.) When this reflected wave reaches the receiving antenna, it tends, in some measure, to oppose the wave which is transmitted directly, and only the difference between the two waves is available to produce a current in the receiving antenna. Thus, even if the path between transmitter and receiver is open and unobstructed, the wave is severely weakened by passage of only a few tens of miles.

If the wave encounters a great obstruction, such as a large building or hill, it is further weakened. The ultimate obstruction is the earth itself, as we can see in Figure 33. If we climb the transmitter

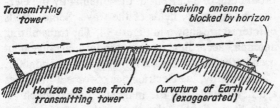

Fig. 33. The curved earth at the horizon forms the ultimate obstruction to television waves. The transmitting and receiving antennas should be as high as possible to permit long-distance reception.

tower and look outward, our line of sight is ultimately blocked by the earth at the horizon. Actually, the horizon for radio waves is somewhat more distant than that for light, since the path of radio waves is slightly curved by graduated density of the atmosphere with increasing altitude. But this is a detail only. Beyond the "radio horizon" the waves are blocked, and only a minute fraction of their energy washes over. We can now see why it is so important to put the transmitter antenna on a high eminence, and why we must put our receiving antenna as high above our chimney as we can get it. If we have a clear line of "radio sight" between the two antennas, the received wave will be reasonably strong, but if the limb (the astronomer's term for the outer edge of a celestial body) of the curved earth obtrudes, the wave will be ready prey to its archenemy—noise.

How the Wave Is Received

We must now look into the final phase of the radio journey, the interception of the radio wave by the receiving antenna. This, as we may by now have guessed, is a simple matter of induction—the production of a current in the antenna by the electric and magnetic fields of the wave. Some details of interest are shown in Figure 34. The transmitting antenna, according to the standard arrangement used in the United States, is a *horizontal* conductor. Consequently, the electric lines of force it produces are horizontal, and the magnetic lines (which always lie at right angles to the current producing them) are vertical. The two fields maintain this alignment throughout their journey. In fact, the surface of our soap bubble, known as the wave

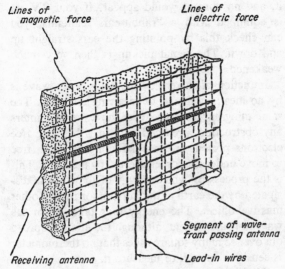

Lines of magnetic force

Lines of electric force

Segment of wave-front passing antenna

Receiving antenna

Lead-in wires

Fig. 34. Electric and magnetic lines of force in the radio wave front induce the signal current in the receiving antenna. You may conceive the wave as approaching from the lower right corner.

front, is everywhere marked by electric and magnetic lines of force in these directions, as shown in the figure.

When the wave front encounters the receiving antenna, the lines of force induce a current in it. For the effect to be a maximum, the antenna must be horizontal, for then the horizontal electric lines of force induce a potential between the ends of the antenna and the vertical magnetic lines induce a current along it. If we were to turn the antenna conductor to a vertical position, the conditions for inducing the current would be wrong. The magnetic lines would then coincide with the conductor, and the electric lines would exert their force across it, and no current would appear. If your TV set is equipped with a "rabbit-ears" antenna, you can check this by pointing the ears straight up and down. The signal pickup is then very much weakened.

Induction of current by the fields of the wave is by no means confined to receiving antennas. The same thing happens whenever the wave encounters any obstruction, provided only that there are free electrons present in the obstructing material, free to move under the forces exerted by the fields. This is the process by which energy of the wave is dissipated by the earth at the horizon, or by any other massive object. The energy thus taken from the wave appears as heat, although the effect is spread out over so many square miles that no thermometer is sensitive enough to measure it.

We have, then, in the receiving antenna a current much weaker than, but otherwise substantially identical to, the current in the transmitting antenna. In other words we have bridged the space gap with a signal current which retains all the information provided by the transmitter. The antenna current is conducted into the living room by the leadin wire and enters the receiver. There it undergoes many manipulations (summarized at the end of this chapter) which separate it from the signals of other stations by tuning, which amplify it and change its form until it is in proper shape to control the deflection currents and the gun of the picture tube.

Modulation and Demodulation

As the last step in understanding the "on-the-air" part of the signal journey we must now look into the processes of modulation, by which the stream of radio waves is made to carry the picture information on its back; and into demodulation by which this information is made to "dismount," so to speak. To understand modulation we must return to the vacuum-tube oscillator circuit (Figure 18, Chapter 3). This produces an extremely high-frequency alternating current which passes through the transmitting antenna and maintains the outgoing stream of waves. If left to its own devices, the oscillator produces alternations of unvarying size, as in Figure 35A. For television purposes the frequency is in the general range of 100 million cycles per second. The trick of modulation is to change the size, or *amplitude,* of the stream of high-frequency alternations from instant to instant, in accordance with the much slower alternations (a few million cycles per second) of the video waveform. This we do by making the vacuum-tube oscillator serve double duty.

We recall that the oscillator works by taking a small part of its output and feeding this back to the input. The tube amplifies this fed-back part, and the magnified portion appears again in the output circuit. The oscillator thus "chases its tail," and the amplitude of the oscillations evidently depends on the amount of amplification imparted by the tube. If we change the amplification, we change the size of the oscillations. We can change the amplification by changing the voltage at the grid. So, if we add the video wave voltage to the grid battery (Figure 35B), we cause the amplifying action of the tube to increase and decrease with corresponding convolutions of the video wave. Then the output oscillations appear as in Figure 35C, and we find in truth that the radio-wave current is carrying the video waveform on its back. The result is called

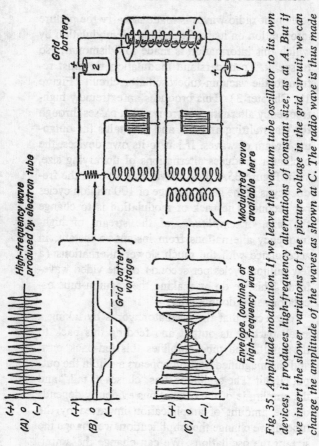

Fig. 35. Amplitude modulation. If we leave the vacuum tube oscillator to its own devices, it produces high-frequency alternations of constant size, as at A. But if we insert the slower variations of the picture voltage in the grid circuit, we can change the amplitude of the waves as shown at C. The radio wave is thus made to carry the picture signal on its back.

amplitude modulation (literally, modification of amplitude).

When the modulated current passes through the transmitting antenna, the strength of the radiated electric and magnetic fields is similarly modulated, and the modulation is preserved throughout the journey to the receiving antenna. Finally, when the high-frequency current is induced in the antenna, it retains the modulations. We have, then, not only bridged the space gap with the radio wave, but by modulation have carried the picture and synchronizing information of the video waveform over the gap.

Throughout the tuning and amplifying operations of the receiver, the modulation is preserved. But, at this point, we must undo the process of modulation and recover the original video waveform. This process, being the reverse of modulation, is called demodulation (or "detection," by an older term which is not very descriptive, since nothing is detected). Demodulation is illustrated in Figure 36. The essential item is a two-element vacuum tube, which passes current in one direction only (page 61, Chapter 3). When we apply the modulated high-frequency alternations to this device, current flows only during one half of each cycle, that half which makes the anode positive with respect to the cathode. (Since the anode is not an emitter of electrons, current cannot flow in the reverse direction when the other half cycles make the cathode positive.)

The half cycles of current pass through the tube to a resistance, across which they develop half cycles of voltage. Connected across the resistance is a capacitor, and the half cycles of voltage charge this capacitor. When the half cycles are increasing in amplitude (as at *b* in Figure 36C) the capacitor voltage increases; when they are decreasing in size (at *a*), the capacitor voltage becomes smaller. Hence, the capacitor develops across itself a voltage which follows only the changes in amplitude of the high-frequency alternations, but does not respond to the individual alternations themselves. The size of the capacitor is chosen, in fact, to be

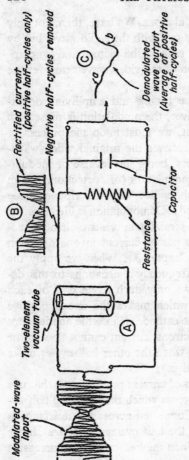

Fig. 36. Demodulation, the process of separating the picture current from the radio wave at the receiver. The two-element vacuum tube A carries current in one direction only and thus removes one half of each high-frequency alternation, as shown at B. The values of resistance and capacitance connected to the tube are too large to follow the high-frequency variations. They take the average of the successive half-cycles, thus recovering the picture voltage, as at C.

large enough to make it incapable of following the very rapid alternations of the radio wave current, but small enough to follow the much slower changes in the video waveform. In effect, the capacitor takes the average of the high-frequency half cycles, and this average is precisely what we are looking for, the original video waveform.

At long last, then, we have completed the journey through space, starting with modulation of the video waveform on a high-frequency current at the transmitter, the radiation of the modulated high-frequency wave, its interception by the receiving antenna, and finally, after amplification, demodulation back into the video waveform. When we add these steps to the cable television system considered at the beginning of this chapter, we have all the parts of the television system as we know and use it, equipped to broadcast programs across the countryside (but not far beyond the horizon!).

Inside the Television Set

We conclude this chapter with a more detailed look at the functions of a television receiver. The block diagram, Figure 37, illustrates the major sections. The first section is the tuner, controlled by the channel selector knob and the fine tuning control. The current from the antenna is first passed to a vacuum-tube amplifier, a part of the tuner, and known as a radiofrequency amplifier. Associated with its input circuit are a number of coils, one of which is switched into position for each channel. The inductance of each coil resonates with its own self-capacitance at the frequency of the channel for which it is intended. A comparatively large coil is needed for the lowest-frequency channel, Channel 2, (54 to 60 megacycles) and a much smaller coil serves for Channel 13 (210 to 216 megacycles). The fine tuning knob adjusts a small auxiliary variable capacitor so that the resonant frequency of the coil and capacitor combination is precisely centered on the frequency of the desired channel.

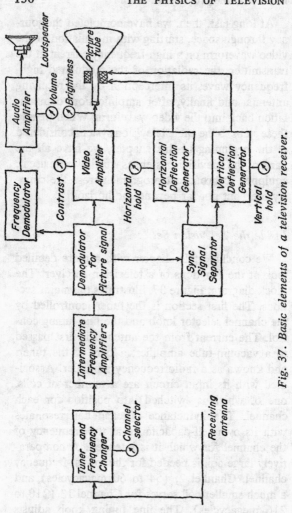

Fig. 37. Basic elements of a television receiver.

From the radiofrequency amplifier, the modulated high-frequency current is passed to a frequency-changing vacuum tube, known as a superheterodyne mixer. The purpose of the frequency changer is to convert the incoming channel frequencies, which vary all the way from 54 to 216 megacycles, depending on the channel selected, to a *fixed* frequency range, between 41 and 47 megacycles. Since the frequencies of all channels are converted to this range, the following amplifiers need not be adjustable to different frequency ranges. Freed of this necessity, these amplifiers can be made extremely efficient. Three or four such "intermediate-frequency" amplifiers follow the frequency changer one after the other. These make the modulated high-frequency signal strong enough to operate the demodulator which follows.

At this point we have recovered the video waveform, and we pass it thereafter along two paths. The first goes to the video amplifier, previously mentioned in this chapter, which raises the voltage of the wave to about 60 volts, sufficiently high to control the electron gun of the picture tube. The contrast control adjusts the amplification at this point. The other path leads to the sync-separation amplifier, which diverts the horizontal and vertical synchronizing pulses from the video wave. These in turn are conducted to the respective deflection current generators, where they control the timing of the scanning process. *Hold* controls associated with each deflection generator are available to bring the deflection into precise step with the incoming signal. The brightness control, connected to the electron gun, adjusts the average current in the electron beam and thus sets the over-all brightness of the image.

The remaining sections of the receiver handle the sound (audio) part of the signal. The sound is processed by a separate circuit in the transmitter, at a different frequency from the picture wave, but both picture and sound waves are broadcast in the same channel, and in the receiver both are selected and amplified simultaneously by the tuner, frequency changer, and intermediate-frequency amplifiers. The sound is carried by a different type of modulation (frequency modulation), by which the current from the microphone causes a slight change in the frequency of the sound-carrying radio wave. The frequency variations are preserved through all the circuits up to the output of the demodulator, and usually they do not interfere with the picture signal because the two forms of modulation are basically different. A separate path from the demodulator conducts the sound signal to a frequency detector, which is sensitive to the small variations in frequency representing the original sound waves. At the output of this detector, we have a reproduction of the microphone current. This is then boosted, by means of an audio amplifier, to a strength sufficient to operate the loudspeaker.

The remaining sections of the receiver are two power supplies. One of these simply converts the 60-cycle power from the wall socket into moderate-voltage direct current needed to operate the vacuum tubes. The other power supply produces high-voltage direct current which is applied to the screen and electron gun of the picture tube to accelerate the beam electrons. As a matter of convenience, this power supply utilizes the high-voltage pulses generated by the horizontal deflection generator during the retrace periods of the electron beam, and smooths them into high-voltage direct current. In this way the horizontal deflection generator is made to serve two separate purposes.

Looking back, we see that the picture signal, in

the process of being amplified, having its frequency changed, amplified again, put through the demodulator, and amplified still again, passes through at least seven vacuum tubes, one after the other. The sum total of the amplification of the signal is enormous. A distant station, say one fifty miles from the receiver, delivers to the receiving antenna only a minute amount of power—roughly a hundredth of a thousandth of a millionth of a watt. By the time this signal has gone through the receiver its power has been amplified to about one watt. In other words, the receiver increases the signal power by roughly one hundred thousand million times! The fact that the receiver can do so, while still protecting the fine details of the picture waveform, is a major achievement of electronic technology.

CHAPTER 6

Color Television

To poets, and indeed to the average person, color seems a matter for simple gratitude, but to philosophers and physicists it presents a durable problem of unsolved complexity.

To begin with, are we to regard words like "blue" and "white" as applicable to physical objects themselves, to the light they radiate or reflect, or to the sensations we experience when that light enters our eye? We talk about the deep blue sea, but those who live near the sea know that it can assume a whole variety of different tints, depending primarily on the weather and specifically on the light conditions. These changes of reflected color with changing light are familiar enough and might impel us to jump at hasty conclusions. We might confidently assert that the white paper of this book would look red under the red light of a photographic dark room, but we would be in for a surprise—it will still look white. On the other hand, blood under the red light of the dark room looks not red but colorless, like water. The impression "white" seems to come from anything that reflects all the illumination present, whatever its composition.

But in our normal experience reflecting objects assume different tints under different conditions of illumination. What we really mean when we assign particular colors to most objects is that they look this or that color under normal conditions. When we see them under unusual light, our memory makes subconscious corrections; we immediately think, "Watch it! Don't be deceived by appearances."

Of course, so far we have spoken only of things that shine by reflected light and not of true emitters. The glow from a mercury vapor lamp is always of the same color, and we also know that the light emitted by the sun has a fixed color composition. Yet, again, the color of such emitters does not always *look* the same. Things can happen to the light on its journey from source to observer, so that it is different by the time it enters our eye. The sun looks yellow at midday and red at sunset because its light is subject to scattering in the earth's atmosphere.

We see, then, that color is a label more commonly applied to the light entering our eye than to the source of the light. Yet even here we run into difficulties. A color-blind person will perceive sensations which are quite indistinguishable when he compares certain light sources that a person with normal color vision asserts to be entirely different. And it is quite possible to trick even people with normal vision into having "misleading" color sensations, if they are put in surroundings which prevent them from making the type of subconscious mental correction mentioned earlier. In one of his lectures a well-known physics professor used to smoke a cigarette under such conditions of semi-illumination that his students "saw" the glowing tip as green. We must therefore make the further distinction between what may be called *physical color,* which describes objectively the wave lengths and energy of light as measured by physical instruments, and *physiological color,* which describes subjectively the resulting sensations perceived by a person. In the physiological sense, what we mean by saying that the sun is orange is that we have a sensation of a round orange patch in our private world of consciousness.

If we eliminate all optical "tricks," several definite and quantitative statements can be made about physical color, and it is to some of these that we next turn. First, there is light of a single pure color called monochromatic. Monochromatic color is directly and uniquely described by its frequency; for instance, red shades have lower frequencies than blue. (See Chapter 2.) Most light that comes to us in nature, whether directly emitted or indirectly reflected, is not monochromatic but includes a continuous range of frequencies. Its color, then, depends not only on which frequencies are present but on their relative intensities. This is expressed quantitatively by means of a so-called *energy distribution curve,* of the type shown in Figure 38. The curve tells us the amount of energy radiated at each frequency, and how this amount varies with the frequency. The total energy radiated is obtained by addition of the energies over all the frequencies; graphically it is proportional to the area lying underneath the curve. Such graphs are found experimentally by passing the incident light through a prism or grating, and examining each band of the resulting spectrum in turn, using a photoelectric tube. The frequency at which maximum emission occurs is called the dominant frequency, and this

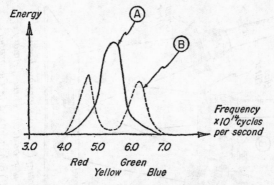

Fig. 38. Colored light is described in physical terms by an energy distribution curve. The typical curve A represents a yellow color having a strong component in the yellow region of the spectrum. The distribution shown in B has components in the red and green regions, and is physically different from that shown at A. But to the eye it is the same yellow.

usually determines the over-all color of the mixture. The commonest white light, which is so-called average daylight, is merely a particular mixture of frequencies with a particular energy distribution curve.

Adding and Subtracting Colors

Now, it is a well-known fact that two or more color mixtures may themselves be combined, and that when this happens an entirely different color is produced. We have known this since earliest childhood. If we did not observe it in our first scribblings with colored crayons, the kindergarten teacher pointed it out in our first artistic strivings with a box of paints. For instance, red and green

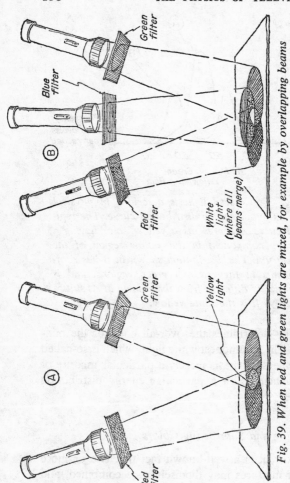

Fig. 39. When red and green lights are mixed, for example by overlapping beams from flashlights fitted with filters (A), yellow light is produced. Three primary colors (red, green, and blue) produce white light (B) when mixed in the proper portions. By altering the strengths of the three primary colors, and by adding or subtracting them, every visible color can be reproduced.

light combine to produce yellow, as is shown in Figure 39. We could anticipate this spectacular change just from examination of the two individual energy distribution curves. If we add them, we produce a new curve with a shape entirely different from either of the two, indicating that a color entirely different from red and green might be expected in the combination. What *is* surprising, however, is that we may create the same yellow light, visually indistinguishable from the first, by combinations of entirely different initial colors. Indeed, we can do so without any combination at all, merely by choosing the appropriate monochromatic frequency of yellow. In all three yellows we therefore have different energy distribution curves; in other words, they are different colors, physically speaking. Yet each produces the same visual sensation; physiologically they are the same color. This is an extremely important general distinction between physical and physiological color, and we shall see later how fortunate it is for the purposes of color television.

Physiological theories of color vision are still in their infancy and largely in the realm of speculation.[1] What is known for certain is that there are two kinds of light-sensitive receptors in the retina of the human eye, rods and cones. Color perception is almost entirely cone reception. This is why in very dim light, when we see exclusively by means of the rods, all objects appear a dull and neutral gray. Recently, physiological if not anatomical evidence has been accumulating in favor of the old idea (previously little more than a guess) that there are three distinct types of cones. It appears that each type of cone contains a different pigment which makes it sensitive to different frequency ranges. Just as we plotted the energy distribution curve for an emitter (Figure 38), so we can for an

[1] Edwin H. Land, inventor of the Polaroid camera, recently has made discoveries about color that seem to contradict current theory and that are yet to be explained.

absorber, only then the vertical co-ordinate measures the energy *absorbed* at any particular wave length. Tentative figures have even been obtained for the dominant wave length for each cone type.

If we now indulge in some pure guesswork, we may reason as follows. We know from the evidence about color mixing already given that the eye is not able to distinguish the separate frequencies in a color mixture. No cone type is able to say, "This light contains so much of this particular frequency, and so much of that." However, it is a reasonable assumption that the cone *is* capable of recording the *total* energy that it absorbs, irrespective of frequency. If we now examine the effect of two different monochromatic light sources on the three cone types, each with its different response curve, we see that the relative total energies absorbed by

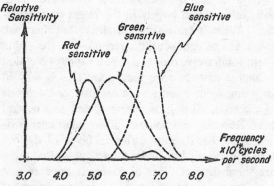

Fig. 40. *Although we don't know precisely how the eye sees color, experts suppose that the retina may have three different kinds of color receptors, with sensitivity curves possibly like those shown above. This would explain the fact that three primary colors, when mixed, can match the whole range of colors throughout the visible spectrum.*

each type are precisely what change (Figure 40). It is therefore possible that physiological color (whatever it is that makes the observer say "orange" in one case and "yellow" in the other) is simply the *ratio* of total energy absorbed by each kind of cone. Any color could then be expressed as a ratio of three numbers, much as it can already be expressed as a ratio of intensities of three "primary" colors. This can be related to color in terms of nerve impulses. Remembering the mechanism of the eye (Chapter 2), we may state that the rate of impulses delivered along any one nerve pathway from the eye is a direct measure of the rate of photon absorption by the receptor cell. Color would thus be expressed as a ratio of nerve impulses coming from the three different types of cones.

This brief speculative excursion has perhaps been justified because of the extreme importance of the experimental findings which we have been seeking to explain. These experiments have long been known, and about them there is no doubt. It is found that a minimum of three primary physical colors, when mixed in varying proportions,[2] will yield any desired physiological color. This includes not only the intense, so-called saturated, spectrum colors, but all the pastel shades as well as white and off-white tints. In certain cases, where simple addition of the primaries (P_1, P_2, and P_3) will not produce a match, subtraction will. One of the primaries, say, P_3, is added to the color to be matched, C, giving the equation $C + P_3 = P_1 + P_2$, which is algebraically equivalent to $C = P_1 + P_2 - P_3$. It should be emphasized that the choice of primaries is highly arbitrary; almost any three will do. But,

[2] The Land experiments mentioned in the previous footnote deal with mixtures of *two*, instead of three, colors.

the dominant frequencies of the three cone types make some choices more convenient than others, in the sense that subtraction is needed less often to match a given color. The generally accepted primary colors for mixing transmitted light are intense shades of red, green, and blue.

How fortunate all this is from the point of view of color television, or indeed of color photography and color printing! If the human eye had the same analytical power of perception as, say, the ear, none of these processes would be possible. The ear can distinguish many of the harmonic frequencies which give sound its distinctive quality and enable us to say whether a given note is being produced by a piano or piccolo, triangle or trumpet. If the eye could similarly distinguish all the component frequencies of a color mixture, then every color would have to be transmitted uniquely, with all the precise features of its energy distribution curve preserved. We should then have to transmit a separate image of the picture for each of the *physical colors* present, and then add them all together at the end. The catalogue of colors in terms of energy distribution would be enormous. It would take literally thousands of pages of graphs and numerical specifications to define all the ten thousand or so colors the normal eye is capable of distinguishing as separate physiological colors. Happily, we are able to counterfeit, as it were, any desired result using only three variables to two places of decimals, and can specify the whole range of *physiological* colors quantitatively in less than ten pages.

Thus, color television, photography, or printing can all, if desired, be reduced to "three-color" processes. Essentially, we make three pictures of the original, one in each of the primary colors, and then recombine them. It is true that the details of color reproduction vary, depending on whether we are using transmitted or reflected light to produce the final image. In the first we have a simple additive process; in the second a subtractive one.

Most color printing is a good example of the latter. We saw in Chapter 2 that reflection from an opaque surface is really a process of selective absorption. The pigments *subtract* from the incident light certain preferred frequencies which are not therefore passed on in the reflected light. Printing ink is merely a solution of a pigment in a transparent solvent. The three "primary" inks subtract the red, green, and blue light, respectively. Since their colors depend on the light they reflect, these are determined by what is left of white light after red, or green, or blue has been taken away from it. Thus white minus red gives a peacock blue; white minus green gives magenta; and white minus blue gives yellow. Hence the primary colors of printing inks (or, for that matter, of paints in a child's paintbox) are blue, magenta, and yellow—different from the red, green, and blue of the additive process.

Electronic Color

In color television, unlike printing, the final picture is produced by an additive process, which works as follows. Three different fluorescent substances are chosen which, when excited by a stream of electrons, glow with a red, green, and blue light, respectively. The picture screen is constructed of a mosaic of tiny dots, rather like a half-tone printing in a newspaper. There are equal numbers of dots of each fluorescent substance, uniformly distributed so that any adjacent group of three forms a tiny triangle containing one "red," one "green," and one "blue." The dots are so small that the members of any one triangle cannot be resolved by the viewer's eye. Their respective fluorescences thus combine additively, and the over-all color of the triangle depends on the relative intensity with which each of the three dots glows. If all three dots glow with appropriate intensity, the over-all result will be white; if none glows at all, the result will be black. Thus a color tube can produce a black-and-white picture, as well as one in full color.

If we can now arrange to produce three primary images of the original picture which is to be televised, one in each of the primary colors, these may be converted into three picture signals, and transmitted to three separate electron guns in the color receiver. Provided that the electrons from the "red" gun are made to fall only on the "red" dots, and similarly for the green and the blue, the intensity with which each dot glows will depend on the strength of the appropriate picture signal. In this way we reproduce on the picture screen copies of the red, green, and blue images recorded by the three cameras.

The three images are separated in the camera by colored filters—for the red image we place a filter in front of the camera lens which subtracts all colors except red, and so on. When the three images are recombined by addition at the receiver, a colored image of the original scene results.

The problem of color television is thus solved in principle, but this is naturally very different from making it a practical proposition. The major technical problems are three. First, we have to arrange for three images, identical in every respect except

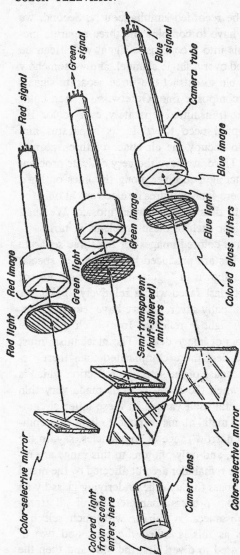

Fig. 41. How the color television camera operates. With color-selective mirrors and filters, the studio scene is focused identically on three camera tubes in the three primary colors.

color, to be recorded simultaneously. Second, we somehow have to combine the three separate picture signals into a composite signal which can be transmitted over a single channel, and we somehow must be able to extract the three separate signals from the composite one. Otherwise, if each color signal were transmitted separately, every color TV station would need to triple its apparatus and would also occupy the air space of three normal channels. Third, we have the very delicate problem of constructing a receiver along the lines outlined above, where each gun fires its electrons at only the appropriate dots on the screen mosaic. We shall now consider each of these problems in turn.

The three-colored images for the three separate camera tubes are produced by a system of special mirrors as shown in Figure 41. A normal mirror consists of glass faced with a relatively thick layer of metal, usually silver, and we have seen in Chapter 2 how light is reflected from such a surface without loss of image detail. The mechanism must be a good deal more complicated than there described, because of the selective reflection which is obtained when the metal layer is made very thin and the metal itself varied. In these latter circumstances the metal atoms respond to light of a comparatively narrow range of frequencies, say, in the blue region, and only photons in this range are reflected. The remainder are not affected by the metal at all, and pass through the underlying glass by an atom-to-atom process characteristic of all transparent substances. A mirror with such selective properties as this is called *dichroic,* and two of them are used to divert first the blue and then the red light in the original image to their respective camera tubes. This leaves only the green available for the third tube.

Brightness and Chrominance

Turning now to the task of combining the three separate picture signals into a single one for transmission, we find that the situation is complicated by the fact that black-and-white as well as color TV sets must be able to receive color transmissions, and vice versa. We get over this by arranging for a simple "brightness" signal to be the basis of both systems; this is in effect a measure of the light intensity, or *luminance*. In addition, in the color system we transmit a second so-called *chrominance signal,* which contains the specific information about color *hue* and *saturation.* A black-and-white receiver can interpret the brightness signal of a colored broadcast while ignoring the chrominance signal. A color receiver, though primarily designed to interpret both signals, can nevertheless produce a black-and-white picture from the brightness signal alone, when tuned in to a black-and-white broadcast.

The production of the brightness signal from the primary color signals is not too difficult. We have already seen that if we wish to add any two signals together, we can do so with an arrangement such as is shown in Figure 42. We apply one signal to the grid of one tube and the second to the grid of another, and then connect the anodes of the two tubes together. The waveforms of the two signals are thereby superimposed. To obtain the brightness signal, we add the primary-color signals from the three camera tubes (Figure 41). If we wish to subtract one from another, we need only reverse the

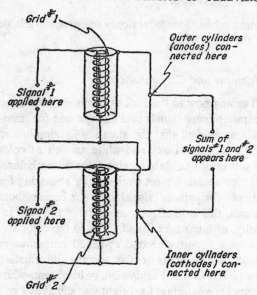

Fig. 42. Two vacuum tubes can add two signals which are fed to their respective grids, simply by connecting their anodes together. Subtraction occurs if we reverse the connections of one of the input circuits. Three tubes with anodes connected combine the three primary color signals produced by the color camera.

connections to one of the grids. In this way we can mix the three primary-color signals, and furthermore, by controlling their relative amplification, mix them in any desired proportions. We know that when mixed in the correct ratio, the three primary colors produce white light, and it is found that a mixture of about 30 per cent red, 60 per cent green, and 10 per cent blue produces an excellent black-and-white picture. This brightness signal is made to amplitude-modulate a carrier frequency in the way outlined in the last chapter.

Now for the chrominance signal. This is what gives the color receiver the additional information to enable it to add color to the black-and-white picture. To produce this we subtract the combined "brightness" waveform we have just been discussing from each of the primary-color waveforms in turn. For instance, in the case of the by now somewhat threadbare blue dress of Chapter 2, the resulting "color-difference" signal would be positive for blue, and negative for red and green. The three "color-difference" signals are then combined to give the chrominance signal. This represents the *differences* between the full-color image and the black-and-white image, or (in a more colorful metaphor if that is possible in such a context!) it can be thought of as a triple message which tells which electron gun in the receiver to step up its activity and which to take it easy. In the receiver, using circuits which operate in the reverse order of those used in the studio, we derive from the carrier the three color-difference signals which are then applied individually to their respective electron guns. These add or subtract brightness for each of the primary-color images, thereby altering their proportion in a way which brings out the color content of the scene.

The chrominance signal is transmitted over the air in the same channel as the brightness signal, but it is made to modulate the stream of carrier waves by a method we have not met before, called *phase modulation*.

Any carrier wave has three characteristics: its amplitude or strength; its frequency or its number of cycles per second; and finally its phase, which describes the degree to which it is or is not in step with a predetermined and fixed time schedule.

We have seen how amplitude modulation changes the strength of a carrier, and how frequency modulation changes the carrier's frequency. Phase modulation advances or retards the time at which each wave of the carrier emerges from the oscillator.

At the receiver this advancement or retardation is detected by comparing the incoming carrier waves with a locally generated carrier, which is identical to and synchronized with the unmodulated carrier of the transmitter. This is similar to comparing one watch which is sometimes set ahead, and sometimes set behind, with another watch which always keeps constant time. The results of this comparison develop the chrominance signal. The color voltages change the phase of the carrier, relative to its unmodulated form, each color doing so by a different amount.

Finally, there remains the problem of arranging that the beam from each of the three electron guns shall hit only the appropriate dots on the viewing screen. This is solved by means of a metal plate pierced with more than 200,000 tiny holes, which is positioned between the guns and the viewing screen. It is known as a *shadow mask,* since, as is shown in Figure 43, the holes in the plate are so placed that it masks the two unwanted dots in each triangular group of three, from any one electron beam. Thus the electrons from the red-controlled gun can fall only on "red" dots, and similarly for the green and the blue. The electron beams are focused so that they converge on any one hole in the mask, by electrostatic means. The deflection necessary for the scanning action is achieved electromagnetically. The over-all arrangement of the shadow-mask tube is shown in Figure 44.

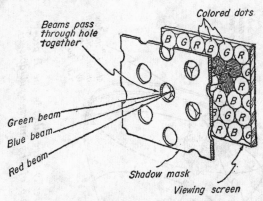

Fig. 43. The three beams in the color picture tube carry the respective picture currents for the red, green, and blue primary images. Each beam strikes phosphor dots of the corresponding color. To keep each beam from straying off to the wrong color, a metal mask, pierced with tiny holes, is placed just behind the viewing screen. This intercepts or "shadows" each beam and confines it to the phosphor dots of the proper color.

TV and the Future

From all this it should be clear that a color TV receiver is an even more delicate and complex instrument than its black-and-white predecessor. Not only does it contain many more components—tubes, capacitors, resistors, and the like—but closer tolerances, finer adjustments, and higher quality are required all along the line. It is for these reasons that color sets have cost about twice as much as their equivalents in black-and-white. Yet, slowly and surely this difference in price will be whittled away, and color TV will become generally availa-

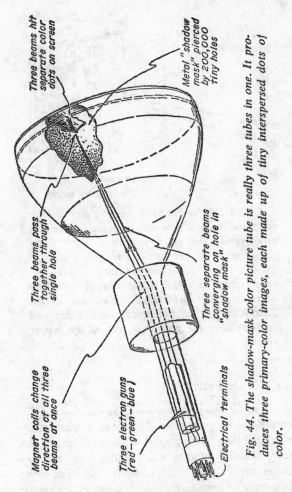

Three beams hit separate color dots on screen

Metal "shadow mask" pierced by 200,000 tiny holes

Three beams pass together through single hole

Three separate beams converging on hole in "shadow mask"

Magnet coils change direction of all three beams at once

Three electron guns (red – green – blue)

Electrical terminals

Fig. 44. The shadow-mask color picture tube is really three tubes in one. It produces three primary-color images, each made up of tiny interspersed dots of color.

ble in homes, schools, and industry. When this happens, we shall have gone a long way toward achieving the ultimate in human communication, which we discussed at the beginning of this book.

There are many people who eye further development of TV with suspicion and regret, and who regard it as little more than a softener of the brain. Certainly, to use TV purely as a form of entertainment for killing time and masking a fundamental boredom with life would be a gross prostitution of the scientific skill and inventiveness which have produced this marvel. But there are many constructive uses of TV, and it is perhaps not unduly pompous to say that someday, when it becomes woven into a world-wide network of communication, TV may prove a decisive influence in helping different nations to understand and tolerate each other.

INDEX